BUILT!

BUILT!

The New Bodybuilding for Everyone

ROBERT KENNEDY & MAGGIE GREENWOOD-ROBINSON

A PERIGEE BOOK

Perigee Books
are published by
The Putnam Publishing Group
200 Madison Avenue
New York, NY 10016

Published simultaneously in Canada by
General Publishing Co. Limited, Toronto

Library of Congress Cataloging-in-Publication Data

Kennedy, Robert, date.
  Built! : the new bodybuilding for everyone.

  Bibliography: p.
  1. Bodybuilding.   I. Greenwood-Robinson, Maggie.
II. Title.
GV546.5.K4453   1987   646.7′5   87-11048
ISBN 0-399-51380-9

Book design by The Sarabande Press
Printed in the United States of America
      4   5   6   7   8   9   10

Contents

Introduction and Acknowledgments

Bodybuilding has been around since antiquity. Is there really anything "new" about it? Definitely! First of all, it is more popular today than ever, with more converts coming into the "muscle fold" every year. Research into the whole weight training area has picked up considerably since the fitness renaissance began a number of years back. New information is coming out all the time on the health-giving benefits of bodybuilding—even to the point of exploding some old myths.

In gyms around the world, people are discovering that bodybuilding gives them a dimension in their quest for physical perfection not to be found with other forms of exercise. And the best part is that it takes less time to get into shape with bodybuilding than with anything else—a real advantage in today's busy world.

People constantly ask us about bodybuilding, especially how to start and what to expect. The answers are all here, from basic to advanced information. We've also included training secrets from the best bodies in the world—professional bodybuilders who have spent years perfecting their own physiques.

Our sincere thanks and appreciation go to those athletes who spent time sharing their bodybuilding knowledge with us: Kay Baxter, Dave Hawk, Jeff King, Todd King, Bill Norberg, Dona Oliveira, Tina Plakinger, Tom Platz, and Marjo Selin. We also wish to thank Mike Carter, vice-president for youth and adolescent activities, National Strength and Conditioning Association (NSCA); Dick Conner, coach of nationally ranked powerlifters and bodybuilders; Dr. Bob Goldman, author and expert on drugs in sports; Dr. Ash Hayes, executive director of the President's Council on Physical Fitness and Sports; Mary Engelland, registered dietitian and a YMCA fitness director; and Nina Schoenbaum, director of the Women's Mid-City Bodybuilding Gym in New York City. These people have provided helpful information and insight into the many facets of bodybuilding, from training techniques to diet to motivation.

In this book we have used pictures of men and women at all levels. Some are merely well developed; others are standard. We are especially indebted to all these bodybuilders. Without them there would be no book.

We would also like to thank the various gyms that always welcome our photographers, and especially Joe Gold of World Gym and Pete Grymkowski of Gold's Gym.

Opposite:
The amazing
Arnold
Schwarzenegger.

To Joe and Ben Weider we take a bow in respect and gratefulness. We are always welcomed to the IFBB shows and encouraged to meet, photograph, and interview the stars of the sport. Bodybuilding has grown to the degree it has principally because of their combined efforts. Their importance is never underestimated.

The exercise section of this book was photographed exclusively by expert lensman Steve Douglas at the Gold's Gym, Mississauga. The model is IFBB World Champion Steve Brisbois.

To our other photographers, we offer special gratitude and appreciation. Thanks go to Chris Lund, Art Zeller, Bill Heimanson, Doris Barrilleaux, Garry Bartlett, Denie Walter, Glenn Low, Mike Neveux, John Balik, Ralph DeHaan, John Running, Paula Crane, Francis Farrugia, Al Antuck, Wayne Gallasch, Bill Reynolds, Russ Warner, Jim Marchand, and our custom film processor, Mike Read.

Chapter 1
Bodybuilding Magic

Matt Mendenhall, U.S.A.

I f you've looked into the mirror lately and found yourself to be less than ideal, you have plenty of company. At one time or another, most of us have told ourselves that we're too fat, too skinny, too short, or too tall. We never quite measure up to the images of physical perfection we see in the media. Maybe life would be a whole lot more pleasurable if we could all trade ourselves in for new models!

Rather than looking into the mirror and bemoaning your less-than-perfect body, figure out what you can realistically do to improve the shape you're in. Do you have toothpick arms? Are your thighs like marshmallows? Is there a spare tire around your waist? You have control over these body flaws. You can *change* toothpick arms, marshmallow thighs, and spare tire tummies. You can take your *whole* body and make it even better. You can come as close to trading yourself in for a new model as you can get. The method is called bodybuilding. And it works.

The Iron Sports

Bodybuilding is an excellent way to get into shape fast. It's a form of weight training—the use of barbells, dumbbells, and machines to make muscle and get strong. In its purely competitive form, *bodybuilding* is one of the "iron" sports. So are weightlifting and powerlifting.

Weightlifting has been a recognized sport since the first modern Olympic Games in 1896. It is a rigorous sport, demanding immense strength and quick, explosive power from its athletes, who must train hard for many years before entering their first competition.

During competition, weightlifters strive for the heaviest poundage possible in two lifts: the "snatch" and the "clean and jerk." Weightlifters must be precise in technique and action.

Weightlifting was once popular in the United States, but since the sixties, the number of Americans participating in the sport has dwindled. Today, the Soviets and Eastern Bloc countries dominate weightlifting.

As the popularity of weightlifting declined in the United States, participation in powerlifting grew worldwide. It is now an internationally contested sport and has been since the 1970s. Powerlifting is easier to learn than weightlifting and requires fewer years of training. In fact, novice powerlifters begin competing within a few months of learning the sport.

Powerlifters are tested in three lifts, the "squat," "bench press," and "deadlift"—three basic weight training exercises. In each lift, they go for the heaviest poundage they can manage. Unlike weightlifting's fast, explosive moves, power lifts are slow and deliberate. Many iron athletes started out as powerlifters and later became bodybuilders. Franco Columbu, professional bodybuilder, chiropractor, and two-time Mr. Olympia, is a famous example of

Opposite: Not too many bodybuilders have the perfect proportion of John Terilli.

an athlete who made this switch. Powerlifting builds an impressive muscular foundation for bodybuilding.

Unlike powerlifters and weightlifters, bodybuilders are judged on how they look, not on how much they lift. Judges want to see well-defined muscle, a symmetrical shape, and masterful posing. To prepare for competition, bodybuilders train hard several days each week for many months. They diet strenuously to rid themselves of fat so that their bodies will appear etched with muscular definition. And they spend many hours in front of the mirror flexing their muscles, rehearsing poses, and assessing and reassessing their progress.

Bodybuilders see their sport as physical art. They like to compare themselves to artists who sculpt statues from clay and marble. Bodybuilders do the same with their bodies. A sculptor uses chisels and mallets; a bodybuilder, barbells and dumbbells. A bodybuilder's goal is to create an aesthetically pleasing physique through careful training and good nutrition.

Years ago, Mr. America–and Mr. Universe–style bodybuilders were the only ones seriously pumping iron. Today, the enormous popularity of bodybuilding and other iron sports has made body buffs out of thousands of men and women. Bodybuilding is a sport and a lifestyle that has cemented fast in our fitness-conscious world.

Start Now

Individuals interested in iron sports frequently ask what age is the right time to start lifting weights. Generally, you can start working out at *any* age as long as good health prevails. But how much progress you make, what exercises you do, and how much weight you lift does depend on certain physical changes that take place in your body over time.

Children and Teens

A youngster who has not yet reached puberty—the time at which sexual maturation occurs in men and women—will have little chance of making the strength and muscle mass gains associated with weight training. Here's why.

When puberty starts, the body's master gland, the pituitary, releases chemical messengers called hormones, which regulate various body processes, including growth. Through hormones, the pituitary tells the rest of the body that it's time to grow up. Everyone reaches puberty at a different age, with girls usually beginning before boys. By age sixteen, most teenagers have reached puberty.

The ability to build muscle is tied to the release of these hormones, specifically testosterone in men and estrogen in women. Both men and

Mohamed Makkawy and Lee Haney.

women have both testosterone and estrogen in their bodies, but in different proportions. Men have more testosterone, which influences the development of large muscles from bodybuilding. Women have greater amounts of estrogen, which stimulates the manufacture of extra fat, and only tiny amounts of testosterone. That's why women who lift weights won't build big muscles.

Before puberty, muscle weight is about 27 percent of a young person's weight. After puberty, the percentage jumps dramatically, to 40 percent. Bodybuilding improves muscular strength and structure even more. When sixteen- and ten-year-old boys were put on an eight-week weight training program in a study conducted in Europe, strength and muscle size increased significantly in every major muscle group in the sixteen-year-olds. The younger group gained strength only in their abdominal and back areas. Their muscles did not get any larger.

Although a prepubertal youngster has little chance of gaining muscle and strength with weights, there are other reasons to start a bodybuilding program. Provided the weights are light and the child is supervised by a qualified coach, bodybuilding will improve muscular flexibility, endurance, and coordination. A youngster's workout should also include sit-ups, push-ups, and chin-ups—exercises that use the body as a weight. These exercises strengthen the torso muscles, giving the spine better support and protection.

During the teen years, individuals can tackle moderate weights with the goal of developing strength and building muscle. Before the age of sixteen, the skeletal system is still growing, so it's best to postpone lifting very heavy weights until age seventeen. Heavy weight training may damage the growth points at the end of a young person's long bones and possibly stunt further growth. Later on (seventeen and older), a person can train with heavier weights, attempt maximum poundages, and work the body with advanced training techniques.

The Twenties and Thirties

If you never had to worry about your shape before, you may now discover that your contours are changing, and not for the better. Your metabolism (your body's food-to-fuel process) is slower than it was when you were a teen, and as a result, extra fat starts padding your physique. Unless you watch your second helpings at mealtime and work out on a regular basis, it will be easier to put pounds on and even harder to take them off.

In your twenties and thirties, your muscles have the potential to perform at their very best. You will be able to lift more and gain more size and definition than at any other time in your life. So why not use those muscles? Now is an excellent time to set the stage for lifetime fitness.

The Middle Years and Later

As you get older, your hormonal balance shifts, and this change influences strength and muscular gains. After menopause in women, estrogen production falls off and male hormones begin to make up a higher share of the hormonal percentage. This means that as a woman ages, she can continue to gain some muscular weight from bodybuilding, adding credence to that once-popular advertising slogan, "You're not getting older, you're getting better."

As a man approaches his middle years, his testosterone levels begin to decline, making it slightly harder for him to keep gaining extra muscle mass. But progress can still be made beyond forty. Albert Beckles, a pro body-builder in his fifties, is one of the many iron athletes with a physique that has defied age. Beckles has beaten many younger bodybuilders in top competitions. "I've found that I'm still making improvements, in spite of the age factor," Beckles commented in the October 1985 issue of *Muscle and Fitness*.

Muscles do not work as well at forty or fifty as they did at twenty or thirty. They lose their flexibility and contractibility with age—two reasons why people who are over forty must take great care when they begin an exercise program for the first time. Another consequence of the aging process is muscular atrophy, the gradual shrinking of muscle size that occurs over time. Bodybuilding helps stall this muscle loss. There is no other form of exercise that does this as well as bodybuilding does. That is why, for both men and women, bodybuilding is a fountain of youth. Without question, it keeps you youthful, strong, and vibrant.

"We all age at a rate encoded in our genes," wrote sixty-year-old body-builder Claude Rigon a few years ago in *Iron Man*. "We can slow up this process significantly if we recognize that the body must be used vigorously and must be fueled intelligently."

A devotee of the youth-giving benefits of bodybuilding, Rigon works out six days a week, eats a balanced, low-fat diet, and has the body of a twenty-year-old to show for it. He serves as just one of many examples of what the bodybuilding lifestyle does for an older person.

The point is that it's never too late to start bodybuilding. You can start as a teenager and have an excellent physique all your life or you can start at fifty, sixty, or seventy and build a body so fit that you put age on hold. No matter what your age when you start, you have much to gain. Here's a preview.

Congratulations all around for the winners of the Nabba Universe in London, England.

Prevent Injuries

If you bodybuild, you'll be less susceptible to sports injuries. That's because bodybuilding strengthens muscles and other tissues, protecting your body from potential damage on the field, track, or court. A recent study showed that weight-trained high school athletes had a third fewer injuries than athletes who did not work out. The weight-trained group recovered faster from injuries than the other group and consequently missed fewer practices. If you're an athlete just beginning a sport, it's wise to start a supervised bodybuilding program at the same time.

Play Better

Not only does bodybuilding help prevent injuries, it also enhances your sports performance. Most top athletic champs are weight-trained winners. And many pros who have successful bodybuilding careers today started lifting weights when they were younger to excel in sports.

To build a team's strength and power, coaches put their players on "strength training" programs. During training sessions, players concentrate on lifting progressively heavier weights to build strength. They also work on conditioning specific muscles that, when strengthened, will make them play better. Strength training forms the core of most major sports programs in high school, in college, and on professional teams. Teams committed to strength training have their own strength coaches.

No matter what the sport, the strongest player has the edge. Strength is the basis for power and endurance. It promotes balance, coordination, flexibility, speed, quickness, and agility. Physical strength has mental advantages too. Just feeling strong gives you the confidence to put forth your best sports effort.

Lose Fat and Gain Muscle

Bodybuilding is somewhat of a paradox in weight control. It helps fat people lose weight and thin people gain it.

For a slender person who wants more size, bodybuilding is a dream come true. Combined with a balanced diet, bodybuilding stimulates muscular growth. Your physique fills out, your shape changes, and before you know it, you've outgrown your clothes.

Gaining muscle mass is also a weapon against fat. Bodybuilding turns muscle cells into little burners that efficiently use up calories—the units of energy you get from food. The more muscular you are the faster your metabolic rate, the speed at which your body processes food and converts it to

Opposite:
Tina Plakinger,
Kevin Lawrence,
and Diana Dennis.

17

energy. Even at rest, a weight-trained muscle burns calories faster than an unconditioned muscle. So when you diet, your body is better able to shed unwanted pounds.

The muscle you ultimately gain through bodybuilding will weigh more than the fat you lose, so don't expect the scales to immediately register that you've lost weight. But you'll look thinner because you have much less fat on your body.

Bodybuilding enhances weight loss in another way too. It is a calorie-burning activity that uses up between three hundred and five hundred calories an hour. By burning these extra calories, bodybuilding helps balance your caloric equation. If you overeat, bodybuilding compensates for the indulgence. If you're dieting, you don't have to cut back on food as much.

Be Heart Healthy

Until recently, weight training was considered to have little effect on the health of the heart because it is an "anaerobic" activity, meaning "without oxygen." Weight training demands short bursts of vigorous work, leaving an "oxygen debt" in the body. This means the cardiovascular system (heart and lungs) cannot meet the oxygen requirements of the working muscles. Exercise such as jogging, swimming, or bicycling is "aerobic," which means "with oxygen." Because aerobic exercise is less intense than weight training, the body can process enough oxygen to support the exercise. Consequently, aerobic exercise can be carried on for longer periods without rest. Aerobic exercise raises your heart rate and prompts your body to use oxygen more efficiently, with the reward being cardiovascular (heart and lung) fitness.

Weight training's reward is muscular fitness. But scores of scientific studies are now showing that the benefits of weight training extend beyond muscle health to encompass cardiovascular fitness too.

Weight training promotes positive changes in the way the heart does its job—changes that are similar to the effects of aerobic exercise. According to various studies, weight training decreases resting heart rate, increases the stroke volume of the heart (the amount of blood pumped out by the heart each beat), and decreases blood pressure. Each of these adaptations means that the heart is doing its job more efficiently and does not have to work as hard to pump blood.

A 1984 study by a team of cardiologists at the University of Oregon found that weight training reduces the levels of LDL (low-density lipoprotein) cholesterol—a dangerous form of cholesterol believed to clog the arteries—and triglycerides, a blood lipid that in high concentrations in the body contributes to heart disease and diabetes. The study also found that weight training slightly increased the level of HDL (high-density lipoprotein) cholesterol,

Opposite: MuscleMag International's publisher and co-author of Built!, Robert Kennedy, shows off the impressive arms of Finland's beautiful Marjo Selin.

18

which has been dubbed the "good" kind because it appears to cleanse the arteries and prevent heart disease.

The increasing body of knowledge on weight training and its benefit for the heart indicates that an exercise program combining weight training with some form of aerobics may greatly lessen your chance of heart disease. But consistency is the key. To get the rewards, you must make aerobics and bodybuilding a lifetime habit.

Pump Up Your Image

Bodybuilding has psychological rewards too. A recent study conducted at Auburn University found that male students who trained with weights for sixteen weeks showed significantly more improvement in self-esteem than a control group who listened to health lectures for the same period of time. Researcher Larry Tucker, who conducted the study, noted that the weight-trained men increased their strength by one-sixth and built more muscular physiques, which made them feel more self-confident.

Tucker believes that another reason why weight training helps improve self-esteem is that, unlike most sports, skill is relatively unimportant. "Musculoskeletal adaption to resistance [the amount of weight lifted]," he writes, "is essentially a guaranteed process, and thus, almost anyone can achieve success while training with weights. The payoffs are not only consistent, but are readily noticeable."

In other words, you don't have to be tall, fast, or supercoordinated to start bodybuilding. You don't have to perform on a court, a field, a course, or a track. You only have to show off the results of your training: a well-built body.

As your outer image begins to improve, so will your inner image. You will like the new "model," inside and out.

Join the Crowd

It's no secret that Sylvester Stallone trained with two-time Mr. Olympia Franco Columbu to hammer his body into fantastic form for the *Rocky II, Rocky IV*, and *Rambo* movies. John Travolta muscle-upped for his role as a dancer in the movie *Staying Alive*. Madonna pumps iron too—even on tour. Bodybuilding greats like Arnold Schwarzenegger and Lou Ferrigno are screen stars in feature films.

Opposite: Training partners Sly "Rambo" Stallone and Franco Columbu.

Nowadays, you see athletes, models, celebrities, and other superstars sporting beautifully muscled bodies. Even department store mannequins are now being molded into muscular figures to reflect today's well-built ideal. Unlike some media images of attractiveness, the athletic look is one you can realistically expect to attain. Muscles are in. It's time to start flexing yours.

Chapter 2

The Feminine Body

The super-shaped Corinna Everson of California.

Pumping iron . . . it used to conjure up images of beefy he-men, streaked with rivulets of sweat, hoisting heavy barbells in a steamy gym. But not anymore. Today, bodybuilding and other iron sports are women's territory too. Women of all ages have learned that the fastest way to a toned-up, trimmed-down figure is by lifting weights. Even exercise class dropouts can find comfort in knowing that bodybuilding requires no special athletic prowess. No matter how butterfingered you are with a basketball, no matter how graceless you are on the tennis court, you can still lift weights, and do it for fitness, for sport, or for both. Bodybuilding's only prerequisites are desire, determination, and good health.

Bodybuilding is one of the most feminine activities you can pursue for good looks. After only six weeks of working out, you'll notice a new image in your mirror. Your body will jiggle less when you wear your bikini. Your jeans will feel looser. Your limp racquetball serve will turn into a mean smash. More muscle tone, less body fat, greater strength—these are the promises of bodybuilding.

Your Muscular Potential

Many women still fear that bodybuilding will make them muscle-bound. Don't worry. Physiologically, you can't muscle up like men can. That's because you have ten times less testosterone in your body than they do. Testosterone is the male hormone that causes a male to physically mature during puberty. Since you have so little of this hormone in your body, you can no more build big muscles than you can grow a beard.

You also have ten times more fat on your body than men do. The reason is that your body manufactures estrogen, which regulates the buildup of fat. This additional fat means you have less muscle in proportion to your total body weight. Extra fat also hides the muscle you do have.

Any muscle size you achieve through bodybuilding only accentuates your body's natural curves. If you do gain what you think is too much muscle, you need only stop working out. Your muscles will simply shrink back to their prebodybuilt condition. Contrary to what many people think, unworked muscle does not turn into fat, because fat and muscle are two completely different types of body tissue. What will change, however, is the ratio of fat to lean body mass, with a greater amount of fat and a smaller amount of muscle. The point to remember is that you control how much or how little muscle your own body is capable of building by the amount of work you do in the gym.

Get Firm

No matter what your age, now is the time to adopt exercise as a way of life. If you don't, you're apt to put on extra weight later. Many women think they can keep fit by dieting alone and try to control their weight with crash, starvation-type diets rather than with exercise. Crash diets lead to food cravings and binges, followed by guilt trips and renewed attempts at starvation dieting. This diet-binge cycle is dangerous. It can result in serious eating disorders such as bulimia, the habit of gorging followed by purging the body by vomiting or overdosing on laxatives; or to anorexia nervosa, the prolonged refusal to eat, resulting in emaciation. Both are life-threatening disorders.

Bodybuilding is a far healthier alternative for figure control than dieting is. After weight training a group of women for a year, physician and pro body-builder Lynn Pirie reported in the August 1986 *Shape* that "the results were dramatic. The women on the average lost 22 pounds of fat and gained seven pounds of muscle for a net loss of 15 pounds—without serious dieting."

Bodybuilding results in lost inches and a firm body. For figure-shaping, it beats calisthenics—jumping jacks, toe touches, and arm circles you've done hundreds of times in your exercise class. The President's Council on Physical Fitness published a study that compared bodybuilding with calisthenics, in which two groups of young women participated in a seven-week exercise program. The results of the study are convincing enough to make you drop your leg lifts and pick up the nearest barbell.

At the end of the seven-week period, the researchers took measurements. The weight-trained women lost inches from their waist, hips, thighs, and arms. The calisthenics group lost inches only from their arms.

As long as you watch your diet, bodybuilding keeps you trim and toned. And good muscular development makes it harder for your body to store fat.

Body Power

Like men, women now lift weights to excel in sports. "Women's athletics is the area where coaches have seen the most dramatic improvements in sports performance. Women who weight train can expect to excel in their chosen sports," says Mike Carter, a coach, powerlifter, and the vice-president for youth and adolescent activities for the National Strength and Conditioning Association (NSCA).

But many women who lift for sports have not entirely embraced the "no pain, no gain" attitude toward training. They approve of the weight-trained look but reject the idea of strength.

Writing in the *Journal of Physical Education, Recreation, and Dance*, Jan Todd, coach and world record holder in women's powerlifting, says that

Juliette Bergman.

female athletes "are weakened by notions that to push hard is unfeminine, that to become too strong will be threatening to the opposite sex. They intellectually understand that increased strength will improve their athletic performance but they don't come to terms with strength as an aspect of femininity. These emotional confusions affect their work in the weight room."

The idea of strength still clashes with traditional images of women as weak, helpless, and passive. But strength is hardly a sexual issue. It is the natural consequence of a physically fit body.

If you're bewildered about the strength and femininity issue, be reassured: You can push yourself to the limit and still never press or curl as much iron as the men you know. That's because men and women have different potentials for strength. Pound for pound, men are stronger than women, especially in the upper body, where a male's broad shoulders give him a decided edge. Men have heavier bones, greater muscle mass, and less body fat than women have. As a rule, men are 30 to 40 percent stronger than women.

You do have the potential to equal a man in lower-body strength, however. That's because women have a wider pelvic area, designed that way by Mother Nature to accommodate childbearing. If you carry excess fat in your lower body—and many women do—your strength potential drops. More fat means less muscle and less strength. And higher amounts of fat impede good sports performance.

Other Female Factors

Whether you train for a sport or work out for fitness, be aware of the effect of menstruation, both physically and mentally, on your performance in the gym. Menstruation influences both strength and motivation.

Throughout your menstrual cycle, the levels of estrogen and its companion hormone progesterone fluctuate in your body, causing monthly mood swings. Some days you'll feel great; other days, you'll feel miserable. During midcycle, when estrogen is high, you'll feel confidently energized. In the gym, you'll be more likely to release total, all-out effort. But during your premenstrual period, a time characterized by low concentrations of hormones, you'll feel tense, anxious, and depressed. Your workouts will feel correspondingly depressed. You may not even feel like working out at all. These ups and downs vary widely among women.

"There are definitely times when I feel worse than others and I might get a little moody," said U.S.A. Champ Suzanne Tigert in the January 1987 issue of *Flex*. "I might feel like I don't want to train. But I've found if I work through it and go ahead and train, I usually feel a lot better afterwards."

Seasoned bodybuilders generally advise that you not worry about the effects of menstruation on your training—after all, it is a natural part of womanhood—and try to get on with your workouts. As Women's Nationals winner Cathey Palyo commented in the same issue of *Flex*: "If I took a three-day break every month, I would never reach my bodybuilding goals." *

Go for It

Despite the physical and psychological differences between the sexes, coaches and athletic trainers urge women to train the same way men do: with intensity and consistency. Take their advice. Don't slow down before the finish line. Explore your individual strength and muscular potential without limits, without fear.

Special Benefits Just for Women

You may not spend much time thinking about your health five or ten years from now. But bodybuilding, started now and continued throughout your life, can make a big difference in how you look and feel later on. In addition to keeping your figure firm, trim, and strong, bodybuilding helps guard against two health conditions that can affect women as they get older: varicose veins and osteoporosis.

Many women get varicose veins—those puffy, twisted blood vessels in the legs—through heredity, pregnancy, obesity, and other factors. Bodybuilding, especially when it emphasizes thigh and calf work, strengthens leg muscles and turns them into a kind of internal support hose, constantly massaging and protecting the walls of veins. This action helps prevent varicose veins.

Osteoporosis is an abnormal loss of bone tissue that afflicts older women after they have stopped menstruating. One way to prevent osteoporosis is to eat ample amounts of dairy foods, which contain the bone-building mineral calcium. Another way is exercise. Any physical activity that tones muscle is an effective prescription against this illness, because exercise improves calcium absorption and stimulates bone formation throughout life. Bodybuilding not only builds muscles, it also builds bone mass.

According to an article in *The Wall Street Journal*, scientists are now trying to figure out why osteoporosis did not exist in prehistoric times, especially since cave dwellers had no dairy foods. Apparently, milk had nothing to do with the prevention of the bone disease. But perhaps physical activity did. Skeletal evidence now shows that people living thirty thousand years ago were taller and more muscular than modern Americans. In prehistoric times, physical activity may have been nature's antidote to osteoporosis.

Having a physically fit, athletic lifestyle pays off in vibrant health now and later. The latest research on women and exercise shows that women who were athletes during their youth and continued to exercise throughout life had a much lower risk of developing cancer of the breast and other reproductive organs. So work out regularly. Enjoy your lithe, lean, and strong body. It's yours for keeps.

The Sport of Women's Bodybuilding

Many women become so thrilled with the changes bodybuilding makes in their figures that they decide to compete. The sport of bodybuilding offers a satisfying competitive outlet even for those who previously had never thought of themselves as being particularly athletic.

In the seventies, women's bodybuilding was a fledgling sport, struggling for identity, acceptance, and recognition. Controversy engulfed it; women flexing muscles was unthinkable, unfeminine. Buoyed by the worldwide fitness craze, the sport slowly gained momentum, came into its own, and built a following of fans that continues to grow yearly. The sport has now entered a second generation—women can work out without risking criticism for building a well-muscled body. Competition is fun and personally rewarding. For many women, the sport has been an entree to other careers.

Pro bodybuilder Gladys Portugues is now a sought-after model who has graced the covers of nearly every fitness magazine as well as the covers of *Ms.* and *American Photographer*. Tina Plakinger has appeared in movies, on a soap opera, and in numerous magazine ads. Pros Lisa Lyon, Carla Dunlap, and Dr. Lynn Pirie—all well-known bodybuilders—have appeared extensively on television as commentators for bodybuilding events, now widely covered by cable and network television.

In today's muscle-conscious world, even the editors of *Vogue* want their models to look as if they've worked out! With muscled beauty in such demand, there are now special modeling agencies that actively seek and promote this popular, ultrafit look.

As a competitive sport, women's bodybuilding is hardly glamorous. It takes dedication and commitment. Competitive bodybuilding means eating salads while your friends are eating pizza. It means sweating for long, grueling hours in the gym, staring at hard-flexed muscles in front of a critical mirror, and choreographing a posing routine and practicing it until you can do it in your sleep. It means sacrificing to keep your body and mind together while training, socializing, working, going to school, or running a household.

Is it worth it? You bet it is. Whether you compete or not, you'll begin to enjoy the changes the demands of bodybuilding are making in your figure. You're redefining your body and cultivating the healthy look of feminine beauty.

Chapter 3
Taking Shape

Mohamed Makkawy.

A reward of bodybuilding is that you get to know your own anatomy better than ever before. Words like *biceps, triceps, pectorals*, and *deltoids* become part of your everyday vocabulary. Dedicated bodybuilders are wonderfully in touch with their bodies, physically and mentally. It's a healthy way to be.

Your Muscles

Your muscular system is a complex arrangement of 650 muscles made up of some 6 billion fibers, each one as thin as a hair but capable of supporting one thousand times its own weight. You possess three types of muscles: smooth muscles, which line your body's organs; cardiac muscle, which pumps the heart; and skeletal muscles, which produce movement. All muscles work the same way—they contract and relax, an action that is possible because muscle fibers can shorten their length by 30 to 40 percent.

Bodybuilding focuses on the development of the 400 skeletal muscles in your body. These muscles work together to move your body's 206 bones. A muscle that has principal responsibility for a given movement is called the *prime mover*. In the barbell curl, a popular arm exercise, the biceps muscle of the arm is the prime mover. Muscles that help produce a certain action but are not the prime mover are called *synergists*.

He's ripped to shreds. Rich Gaspari goes for broke in the single arm row movement.

Muscles are arranged according to *antagonistic* pairs—muscle groups that oppose each other. The biceps, which bends the arm, and the triceps, which straightens it out, are a good example of a pair of antagonistic muscles.

Skeletal muscles begin and end near joints, the juncture where two bones meet. Each muscle has an *origin*—the point on the bone where the muscle is anchored—and an *insertion*, where the muscle is attached to the bone it moves. Using the arm as an example again, your biceps originates at the shoulder joint and inserts on the forearm. So when you bend your elbow, you raise your forearm while your upper arm stays in place.

Skeletal muscles are attached to bones by *tendons*, tough fibrous bands of tissue that are very strong and do not stretch easily. *Ligaments* are like tendons, except that they connect bones at joints. Bodybuilding strengthens your tendons and ligaments.

Making Muscles Grow

Muscles tone, grow, and strengthen when you force them to do more work than they're used to doing. This means working them progressively against resistance. The resistance can be the weight of a barbell, a dumbbell, an exercise machine, or in some cases, your own body. If you make your muscles lift, push, or pull against increasingly heavier resistance, they respond by becoming bigger and stronger. If you increase the number of times you lift a weight (called *repetitions* or *reps*), or the number of *sets* (a grouping of reps) you do, your muscles will grow too. When you progressively and gradually increase weights, reps, or sets, you increase the *intensity* of your work. Greater intensity means a better physique. You never want your muscles to get used to the amount of work they do, or they won't develop the way you want them to.

Physiologically, muscle growth or *hypertrophy* is a result of an increase in the size of muscle fibers. The number of fibers does not increase, for that number has been genetically determined. Intense, progressive weight training is the fastest way to activate this growth. Mild exercise, such as calisthenics, uses very little resistance and thus produces only limited growth.

Progressive weight training also builds strength—the ability of a muscle or group of muscles to exert force during muscular contraction. Muscular strength varies from muscle to muscle. When you increase the strength of a muscle, you also increase its speed of movement—one reason why athletes benefit so greatly from weight training.

Have you ever seen a person who does not have much muscle mass but can demonstrate great strength when lifting a weight? Having huge muscles does not necessarily correlate with strength. A person's overall strength comes not only from muscular fitness but also from the strength of the body's tendons and ligaments.

Strength is often confused with power. The two concepts are related, but different. Power is strength times speed. If you can move a heavy object faster than someone else across the same distance, you are more powerful. Power is a necessary athletic attribute in explosive events, such as sprinting or vertical jumping—movements that demand short, quick bursts of effort. It can be improved by combining weight training with drills specific to an athlete's sport.

Another effect of progressive training is muscular endurance—the capability of a muscle to repeat a certain movement over and over again against moderate resistance. Muscular endurance is linked to cardiovascular fitness, because it requires lots of oxygen and blood.

Your Personal Mold

In both sexes, how much muscle a person gains from bodybuilding depends largely on inherited body type. For instance, if you have a square, muscular frame, your body type is *mesomorphic*. Typically, mesomorphs easily build muscle because they have a larger-than-average number of muscle fibers.

On the other hand, if you are an *ectomorph*—a person with long limbs, little body fat, and few curves, you will have a harder time building much muscle because you have less muscle to start with. But this does not imply that bodybuilding won't benefit an ectomorph. Quite the contrary, bodybuilding endows lanky bodies with fuller, more symmetrical shape.

If adjectives like *soft, round*, or *pudgy* best describe your physique, you have an *endomorphic* body type. Endomorphs tend to gain weight easily but can also gain a fair amount of muscle by bodybuilding, which in turn helps them keep their weight better under control.

The words *ectomorph, mesomorph*, and *endomorph* only describe tendencies toward a certain body type. In reality, most physiques are mixtures of these types. As a bodybuilder, you want to minimize endomorphy (reduce fat) and maximize mesomorphy (build muscle mass), trying ultimately to build the best physique you can from your own genetic endowment. Do not try to become the next Arnold Schwarzeneggar or Rachel McLish. Work out to see what *you* can become, to take your body to its very own physical potential.

Opposite:
Seated pulley rows as performed by superstar James DeMelo.

Get Started

The first major decision you make when you start bodybuilding is where to train, at home or at a gym. There are pros and cons to each choice. Many famous bodybuilders started out training at home. In fact, Mr. America/Mr.

Universe Jeff King says his best workouts were always the ones at home in his basement, where there was no one to distract him.

Bodybuilding pro Dave Hawk recommends that newcomers to bodybuilding train for at least a year at home. "Working out there gives you a chance to discover if you really like bodybuilding, before you spend the money to join a gym," Hawk says.

Home training is also a good option for women who are self-conscious about their bodies and feel intimidated when they go to gyms and see other women, usually thin ones, all dressed up in body-clinging leotards. Get into better shape at home first, and then when you feel more confident about your looks, go to a gym.

If you decide to work out at home, you must invest in some equipment: at the very minimum, a set of barbells and dumbbells, along with a sturdy flat exercise bench.

Working out at home takes some discipline. If you don't have the motivation to do it at home, commit yourself to a gym membership.

Gyms have a number of advantages. You have more equipment to work out on, there are usually people to help you with your bodybuilding program, and it is inspiring to train around others who are just as dedicated to building a better physique as you are.

As you consider joining a gym, ask yourself these questions: Is the cost of a membership affordable? Is the gym close to where I live? How well equipped are the facilities? Are the hours convenient for me? Does the staff seem to be friendly, helpful, and well-trained? What sort of fitness testing or medical exam (if any) does the gym require for new members? Are the members the sort of people I'd like to meet? Will I have to sign a two- or three-year membership contract to join or can I get another type of membership, such as monthly, six-month, or yearly? These are all important considerations. Before you commit yourself, be sure to tour the gym and use the facilities for a trial workout.

Body Tools

Many people join gyms or purchase equipment to use at home and for whatever reason—lack of motivation or poor instruction—end up as exercise dropouts, losing out on the full benefits of their investment. Don't let this happen to you! The more you know about weight training equipment, the better you'll be at determining the best facility to join or the right equipment to purchase, and the more successful you'll be at getting yourself into shape. Familiarize yourself with bodybuilding's "tools of the trade."

Opposite:
The ultimate shape:
Bob Paris.

FREE WEIGHTS are dumbbells and barbells. Used by athletes and fitness buffs for over a century, free weights are the basic tools you need to start sculpting your physique. Dumbbells are small and short, come in pairs, and range in weight from two pounds to one hundred pounds. Some dumbbells are adjustable, meaning you can change the poundage by adding weight to or subtracting weight from the bar.

Barbells come in various sizes, lengths, and weights, the largest being the Olympic bar, which without plates weighs about forty-five pounds. You can add plates ranging in weight from two to forty-five pounds to the bar. Circular fittings called collars anchor the plates to each end of the bar and prevent the plates from sliding off during an exercise. Collars are also used on adjustable dumbbells. Other barbells, those shorter than the Olympic bars, are *fixed*; that is, the plates are permanently secured to the bar. These barbells weigh from twenty pounds to one hundred pounds. Some barbells feature a wavy bar between the two plates. This barbell is called a *cambered bar* or *E-Z curl bar*. Its design eases your grip on certain arm exercises.

Free weights are versatile. There are hundreds of exercises you can do with them. Having a strong repertoire of free weight exercises will keep you from ever getting bored with bodybuilding, because there are so many routines you can create with dumbbells and barbells.

CABLES, like free weights, are also versatile and work virtually every part of your body. A cable apparatus is attached by a pulley to a weight stack so that you can adjust the amount of weight you are using. An array of attachments comes with most cables: ankle straps for hip and thigh work, handles, ropes, and bars for upper-body work.

Cables provide smooth, consistent resistance throughout the exercise, work body parts from any desired angle, and are effective for working specific muscles that need extra shape-up attention.

WEIGHT STACK MACHINES are the most common exercise machines found in gyms today. They feature a stack of weights that can be adjusted according to the amount of resistance you want to lift. Simply insert a pin in the stack and you're ready to work. Machines are designed to stress specific muscles by guiding you through a specific *range of motion* (the full path of a repetition, from beginning to end and back again). There are many manufacturers who produce weight stack equipment, including Nautilus, whose well-engineered line of machines has set standards for the fitness industry.

Nautilus popularized a technology called *variable resistance*. Depending on the machine, the resistance increases or decreases at different points of the exercise. This is possible because Nautilus machines employ a kidney-shaped cam that changes the tension as you perform the exercise, resisting the most where you are strong and the least where you are weak.

Besides pumping iron, you can now pump air or even water. Some gyms are equipped with ultra-modern machines that use either air or water compressed in a cylinder to supply the necessary resistance. Although these high-tech models use different technologies than conventional weight stack machines, they have the same aim: to build muscle.

Well-equipped gyms also have a full selection of *generic equipment*: flat benches, incline benches, chinning bars, and abdominal slant boards. You can use this equipment for stomach work, for dumbbell and barbell exercises, and for certain cable exercises.

Compound and Isolation Exercises

When an exercise involves several muscle groups, it is called a *compound* or a *basic exercise*. Most barbell exercises are compound. When an exercise works a specific muscle or even part of a muscle, it is called an *isolation* exercise. Many dumbbell, cable, and machine exercises are isolation movements. Generally, compound exercises are used for building mass and strength, while isolation exercises are used for defining and shaping muscles.

Free Weights or Machines?

Most bodybuilders, powerlifters, and serious athletes prefer to work out with barbells and dumbbells. Free weights, especially barbells, have a number of advantages over machines.

"Barbells are best for adding muscle size and for building a strong overall muscular foundation," said Arnold Schwarzenegger at a bodybuilding seminar. As compound lifts, barbell exercises call both prime movers and synergist muscles into the action, stimulating greater growth and strength. The overall body balance it takes to perform barbell exercises also promotes gains. Balance and multiple muscle action use up lots of energy too. Therefore, barbell work potentially burns more calories than other weight training movements.

Barbells remain the most popular piece of equipment, despite the advertising claims of machine manufacturers. Actually, every weight training exercise, whether performed with a dumbbell or on a machine, is a variation of some barbell lift.

Barbells and dumbbells allow the body to lift and move in natural ways, whereas machines dictate the way the body must move. Most machines have been designed to fit a man's build, too, and often do not suit a woman's body or even a young person's body. But free weights are for everyone.

In sports, many coaches like to train their athletes with free weights. "Free weights better duplicate an athlete's movements," says the NSCA's Mike Carter. "Machines have their place in athletics, but mainly as supplementary equipment or for injury rehabilitation. Machines are very safe too. It is almost impossible to hurt yourself on a machine if the exercise is performed properly."

There are certain machine exercises that are as integral to weight training as barbells are, including the leg curl, an exercise that develops the back of the legs; the leg press, a move that builds the thighs; calf raises, for the lower leg; and the lat pulldown, a popular exercise for the upper back. Beginners should first master basic barbell and dumbbell movements, use them as primary exercises in their workouts, and later add machine exercises to their routines. Don't fool yourself into thinking that equipment builds the body, it is the effort behind the weights that makes muscle. All equipment works, if you work it hard.

Now that you are familiar with your muscular anatomy and the tools to build it, you're one step closer to a stronger, more fit body.

Chapter 4
Working Out

Tony Pearson.

Building a spectacular body also starts with knowing how to work out safely so you don't wind up in physical therapy before you've had the chance to build even the slightest biceps . . . with learning why it's crucial to lift with ultrastrict form . . . with realizing why the amount of time you spend in the gym does not equate to the size of your muscles. These points may sound like pure common sense to you, but you'd be surprised at how often they go unheeded. Look around the gym some day. You'll hear the startling clang of iron plates hitting the floor because someone forgot to use the collars. You'll find trainees working out so fast that the weight stacks move up and down like pistons. You'll see others "bombing" and "blitzing" themselves into exhaustion. In reality, actions like these only hinder progress. For the very best results, it's important to learn and practice certain basic bodybuilding techniques.

Be Safe

Iron demands respect. That's why barbells, dumbbells, and machines come with various safety features. The collars on barbells and dumbbells keep the plates from sliding off the bar. Certain benches have rails to catch the bar before it can trap you after a failed lift. Racks for performing a lower-body exercise called the squat let you easily load the bar onto your shoulders and then rerack it with minimal energy after you've completed a set. Machines are equipped with straps and seatbelts to keep your body properly aligned during exercises. They're also engineered to adjust to individual heights—a feature that is both a safety consideration and a design element to guarantee that the machine properly works the muscles.

Whether you work out at home or in a gym, use these safety features. They're meant to guard you from injury and to keep you away from ice packs and deep-heat muscle ointment.

Warming Up

It's a good idea to warm up before your workout. Hitting the weights with a cold body leads to muscle tears, pulls, and strains. A proper warmup heats up your muscles and readies your body for the muscular demands of training. Warmups also prepare you mentally for your workout.

Traditionally, stretching was thought to be the best way to warm up, but new research says that stretching cold muscles may hurt the connective tissue within the joints. If you want to stretch, you still have to warm up first.

Many bodybuilders warm up by doing five to ten minutes of light exercise— calisthenics, running in place, rebounding on a minitrampoline, or riding a

Opposite:
Arnold
Schwarzenegger.

stationary bicycle. Called a *general warmup*, these activities are a good way to stoke up your muscle temperature.

Other bodybuilders do a warmup set with a very light weight before each exercise. This method is called a *specific warmup*. Specific warmups pump blood to muscles, raise the temperature of muscle and connective tissue, and provide a rehearsal of the upcoming set. Light aerobics, warmup sets, or a combination of the two are excellent insurance against injury.

The Right Way to Lift

As important as safety features and warmups for preventing training injuries is proper lifting technique. Some beginners think you have to lift weights fast to benefit. Not true! Bodybuilding is one of the few athletic activities that does not require speed. In fact, all lifts are performed slowly. Yanking and jerking the weights only hurts the muscles, joints, tendons, and ligaments.

Both the raising motion of a lift, referred to as the *positive*, and the lowering motion, called the *negative*, should be smooth and controlled. Accentuate the negative, being careful not to let the gravitational momentum pull the weight down too fast. Control each repetition in strict fashion throughout its range of motion.

Bodybuilding pro Jeff King says strict form, more so than poundage, is the way to trigger muscular growth. In fact, he advises that you drop twenty to thirty pounds on any one exercise and instead concentrate solely on perfect form. That way, your muscles get maximum stimulation from every exercise. Three-time Mr. Olympia Lee Haney has the same philosophy. "One rep is two reps, if you do it right," he says.

Although many exercises require different grips and foot positions, a few basics apply to all exercises. Generally, your grip on the bar or machine should be firm, not too tight. If you squeeze the equipment, you're wasting valuable energy that could be exerted in the exercise. In standing exercises, distribute your weight equally on each leg. This will prevent you from wavering, falling backward, and possibly injuring yourself. And bend your knees slightly to protect your lower back. Whether you stand or sit to perform an exercise, practice good posture, with shoulders back and torso erect.

Proper breathing is essential too. With each repetition, inhale just before the lift and exhale as you complete it. Try to synchronize inhalation and exhalation rhythmically with the motion of the exercise, being careful not to hold your breath. Holding your breath cuts the oxygen supply to your blood and, coupled with the exertion of the lift, could result in lightheadedness or even fainting.

Diana Dennis and
Marjo Selin.

Lifting Belts

Many bodybuilders, powerlifters, and weightlifters wear thick leather lifting belts when they work out. The purpose of the belt is to protect your lower back when performing certain heavy lifts, particularly squats, power cleans, overhead presses, and deadlifts. By wearing a belt, you can lift heavier weights, ultimately leading to greater gains.

A belt does not correct poor form, however. That's why many coaches and instructors prefer that beginners not wear belts until six to eight months into their training, after they have perfected proper lifting techniques.

Join Forces

A surefire guarantee for a safe and intense workout every time is to train with a responsible partner, someone who knows proper lifting form and safe exercise performance.

Arnold Schwarzenegger is a great believer in training partners. In 1975, while preparing for the Mr. Olympia, he needed a training partner. His regular partner, Franco Columbu, was going to school and working out at night, and so was unavailable. Schwarzenegger wanted a partner like Columbu, someone eager for victory. Not just anyone would do. One day he heard bodybuilder Ed Corney say "I'm going to beat Franco in the Mr. Olympia short class this year!" That was all Schwarzenegger needed to hear. Corney obviously had the hunger. The two became training partners that year.

"I don't believe you can train properly by yourself," the seven-time Mr. Olympia commented at a bodybuilding seminar. "You've got to choose the right person, someone as hungry and as strong as you." At one time, he used two training partners, Dave Draper for his upper body and Franco Columbu for his lower body.

A partner spurs you on to additional reps, better sets, and more intense workouts. Besides, it's fun to have someone to train with each week. Partner training keeps you both on a consistent, muscle-building schedule.

Not everyone trains with a partner, though. The decision to do so is largely an individual one, but certain heavy exercises, such as squats, bench presses, and shoulder presses, do require assistance from a partner, called a *spotter*.

Spotting carries responsibility, says the National Strength and Conditioning Association's Andrew Fry, writing in the *NSCA Journal*. Among the tips he outlines are these:

- Communicate in advance with your partner. Know the number of reps to be attempted and, if necessary, decide on nonverbal signals to be used.
- On barbell exercises, help load the bar properly, with both ends weighted equally, the plates pushed into their proper position, and the collars fastened securely in place.
- Watch your partner's form at all times, offering positive, constructive criticism.
- Encourage your partner to go for additional reps.
- Concentrate on the exercise, avoiding distractions in the gym. Be ready for the slightest falter.
- Use both hands for spotting and assisting, especially on bench presses and dumbbell exercises.
- On dumbbell exercises, assist by gently pushing on your partner's elbows. Should your partner fail, be quick to grab both weights.
- After your own set, rest before you spot so that you have the energy to devote your full attention to your partner's set.

Personal Trainers

One way to push yourself to new limits and keep your motivation high is to hire a personal trainer, an experienced fitness instructor who works with clients individually, either at home or at the gym, to help them achieve their physique goals. Personal training was once thought to be a luxury only the rich and famous could afford, but now many gyms across the country are offering the service at more affordable rates. It still can be expensive (seventy-five dollars an hour is one of the higher rates) but it is worth looking into, especially if you're someone who needs an extra nudge.

Pro Kay Baxter is bodybuilding's most famous personal trainer, best known for training rock superstar David Lee Roth. She emphasizes the importance of finding a qualified trainer and offers this advice:

- A good personal trainer should have a strong overall knowledge of fitness and be able to advise you not only on bodybuilding but also on proper nutrition and healthy habits.
- Look for someone who can give you an honest assessment of your body and can then plan a program that, if followed religiously, will ensure the desired results.
- Watch out for self-styled trainers out to make some fast money. Investigate a personal trainer's credentials. Ask such questions as: How many years have you trained? Do you have a degree in physical fitness or in a related field? If your goal is to compete in bodybuilding competition, find out if the trainer holds any titles. A personal trainer who is a competitive bodybuilder can also help you with the finer points of contest preparation, from posing to diet.
- Very important in choosing a personal trainer is how that person looks. You want a trainer who is in excellent shape, with all the qualities of physique you desire to attain.

A Balanced Body

Bodybuilding puts your physique in line. The hundreds of exercises available to you are each designed to build specific muscles or groups of muscles. You have the freedom to choose those exercises that will best forge your body into the shape you desire. You can add or subtract size anywhere on your body, working to resculpt your physique into better, more symmetrical proportions. You can get rid of soft, flabby body parts and replace them with firm, muscular dimensions. The body you want is now on the way. The next five chapters cover all the exercises you need to know, plus tips on how to use them to your best advantage.

Chapter 5
Leg Work

Rachel McLish.

An old-time wrestler and strongman named Henry Steinborn immigrated to the United States from Germany after World War I and brought with him a "new" exercise that was to revolutionize weight training the world over because of the spectacular gains in both mass and strength it produced in all who tried it. The magical exercise was the squat.

Early on, *IronMan* began to report the wonders of the squat by publishing inspiring accounts of early weightmen who were making fast progress with it. Peary Rader, the magazine's founder and former editor, had once put on seventy pounds of body weight in two years as a result of a twice-a-week squatting routine. In a series of articles, Rader proclaimed the squat "the greatest single exercise."

The squat deserves that description. It is the best exercise for developing the legs and hips, and because the squat involves so many muscle groups, it also builds the back, chest, arms, and neck. The squat is a key exercise for developing athletic strength and power.

In the first few years of your training, include squats in your routine to build lower-body size and strength. A word of caution here: Enlist the help of a knowledgeable trainer who can guide you in proper squatting technique. "Learning how to squat by yourself is like learning how to fly an airplane alone. You can get into trouble," says Dick Conner, gym owner and trainer of several nationally ranked powerlifters. "The squat is an exercise that should be coached."

Later on in your training program, after you've developed your legs to your personal liking, you may want to drop the squat from your routine and replace it with exercises like leg presses, leg extensions, and hack squats, to bring out visual detail in your legs.

Lower-Body Anatomy

When bodybuilders talk leg training, they mean thighs, hamstrings, hips, and calves—about half the body. That's a lot of anatomy!

The frontal thighs house several muscles, including the sartorius, the longest muscle in the body. The sartorius runs diagonally across the front of the thigh from the hip to just below the knee. It rotates and raises the leg. The sartorius is very visible in the legs of well-trained competitive bodybuilders.

Also part of the frontal thighs is the quadriceps femoris, a group of four muscles used to extend the legs. Bodybuilders refer to this muscle group as the *quads*.

The adductors are the muscles of the inner thigh. They act to rotate the thigh and pull it in toward the body.

The hamstrings are three muscles at the back of the thigh, the largest of which is the biceps femoris or leg biceps. The hamstrings flex the knee and rotate the leg. In sports, the hamstrings are used for running, sprinting, and back kicking in soccer.

The gluteus maximus, gluteus medius, and gluteus minimus make up your hips. These muscles help move the thighs in a variety of directions and are important in athletic moves such as sprinting. Bodybuilders call the hip muscles the *glutes*.

Calf Builders

The major muscles of the calf are the gastrocnemius, a two-headed muscle that runs the back length of the lower leg, and the soleus, a broad flat muscle just beneath the gastrocnemius. Always in action for standing, walking, dancing, and jumping, calf muscles can be stubborn to develop. The muscle fibers of the calves are thick and dense and therefore require several sets of hard, heavy exercises each training session to hammer them into that desired form bodybuilders call *diamond-shaped*. If your calves start to lag in development, here are pointers to help you build them up:

- Practice good form. On calf exercises, raise your heels as high as possible and stretch them as low as possible to obtain an extreme range of motion.
- Work your calves with a training technique called *trisets*, which use a different exercise for each set and are performed without rest between exercises. Three exercises make up one triset. Rest after performing one triset, and then try to complete one or two more trisets. Use very light weights with this technique.
- Change your calf exercises frequently to trigger the muscle into further growth.
- After completing your last set of calf exercises, go for as many partial movements (also called *burns*) as you can, pressing up from the bottom of the exercise to halfway. This action gives your muscle fibers extra stimulation.
- Try Tina Plakinger's remedy for underdeveloped calves. In one of her early amateur contests, she had to compete against a former cheerleader whose best body parts were her calves. Plakinger figured her opponent's well-built calves came from all the jumping up and down cheerleaders do. Needing to bring her own calves up to competitive levels, she started jumping rope. It proved to be an excellent calf builder.

Opposite: Alternate dumbbell curls done the Rich Gaspari way.

THE EXERCISES

Squat

Bodybuilders, powerlifters, and other iron-trained athletes are all devout squatters. In fact, super legman Tom Platz says the squat rack is so much like an altar to him that he feels like kneeling before it as he readies himself for a set. "And once I'm into a good set of squats," he says, "my life passes right before my eyes!"

As Platz attests, the squat is an intense exercise. It directly stresses the thighs, glutes, adductors, and hamstrings. Women who use the squat consistently in their routines will find their legs and hips—typically a woman's most worrisome body parts—taking on firmer, more shapely dimensions.

To begin the squat, take a wide grip on the bar. Dip under the bar, loading it onto your shoulders behind your neck. Your stance is important. Wide footing places greater stress on the hips. A too-narrow stance hinders proper technique. The best stance is one with feet shoulder-width apart, toes angled out, and heels placed on a one-inch block of wood.

Keeping your spine erect and head up, slowly bend your knees and lower yourself until the tops of your thighs are just parallel to the floor. Stand slowly back up, return to the starting point, and repeat the movement. Breathe

deeply during the exercise, inhaling before you descend and exhaling as you stand up. To support your lower back, wear a lifting belt while squatting.

Some gyms have a device called a *natural squatting bar*. It features two padded parallel supports that extend perpendicularly out from the middle of the bar and are designed to rest on the lifter's shoulders. Both ends of the bar, where the weight is carried, are bent down and out, on a line about four inches below the main bar.

Because of its design, the natural squatting bar has several advantages. First, the padded supports are comfortable for the shoulders and lower neck. Second, balance is easily maintained, a factor that eliminates the tendency to hunch forward—an action that could injure your lower back. And third, lifters can apparently break through sticking points much easier with this bar, enabling them to later handle heavier poundage than with the conventional squat and ultimately make greater gains in strength and muscle mass.

Beginner's Squat

Not every beginner should attempt a regular squat, at least not at first. People with back problems or out-of-shape beginners who have never before ex-

ercised must be extremely careful about working out with a lift like the squat. If you fit one of these categories, you might want to try a version of the squat that bodybuilding pro and personal trainer Kay Baxter starts her new students out on, the beginner's squat.

With the help of a coach or trainer, place a light bar (without weights) onto your shoulders. Sit on a flat bench or chair and position your feet on the floor about shoulder-width apart. Then slowly stand up, keeping your back as straight as possible. Now lower yourself back to the starting position, just barely touching your buttocks to the bench. Continue for at least six to twelve reps or as many reps as you can manage.

"This exercise is very safe," Baxter says. "It reduces the potential for low back injury in people who are weak in that area. You do not have to worry about losing your balance either. The exercise also teaches you the strict technique required by a regular squat. Plus, it works the hips, thighs, and lower back very effectively."

As her students become more proficient in this type of squat, she has them place their feet on a board to perform the exercise. This allows them to squat a little lower for a greater range of motion and deeper stress on the hips and thighs.

"I can do more dips than you!" Friendly competition by Rich Gaspari and Frank Richard.

Front Squat

The front squat is performed in the same manner as the regular squat, except that you hold the bar in front of your neck rather than behind it. This exercise works the same muscles as the squat, but because of the change in the placement of the barbell, it zeroes in more directly on the lower thighs, just above the knees. Mr. Olympia/Mr. World Samir Bannout uses the front squat regularly as a thigh shaping exercise in his leg training program.

At the rack, position the bar across your shoulders and upper chest. Once positioned, the bar can be held in one of two ways. Either fold your arms across the barbell and balance it across your upper chest or hold the barbell with your palms facing up and your elbows held straight out, just at shoulder level. With your back erect and your head up, slowly bend your knees, squatting until the tops of your thighs are parallel to the floor. Straighten your legs to return to the starting point, and repeat. Breathe as you would with the regular squat.

Hack Squat

Performed on a special machine called the hack slide, this version of the squat isolates the frontal thighs. The hack squat is an excellent exercise for carving muscle separation in your thighs.

Position yourself in the machine so that your feet are about a foot apart and your shoulders fit comfortably under the pads. Depending on the design of the machine, you'll start the exercise from either a squatting or standing position. Slide up and down in the machine with a slow but steady rhythm. If you want to better isolate the quads, lower yourself to a half-squat, so that your thighs are just parallel to the platform.

By varying your foot position from set to set, you can change the emphasis of this exercise. For example, model/bodybuilder Gladys Portugues does several sets of hack squats with her legs pressed together in order to work her outer thighs more completely. Another trick is to turn your toes outward with heels touching—a stance that works your inner thighs intensely.

Leg Press

Another powerful thigh builder is the leg press. This exercise requires a special machine, which comes in three designs: seated, incline, and vertical.

To perform the *seated leg press*, sit in the machine and place your feet on the pedals. Your knees should be bent and fairly close to your chest—a position that can be set by adjusting the seat lever on the machine. Push forward with your legs, without locking your knees at the top, in order to keep tension on your thighs throughout the movement. Slowly return to the starting point and repeat.

The *incline leg press* is situated at an angle to the floor. Place your feet about a foot apart on the sliding platform. Straighten your legs, release the stops, and slowly bend your knees as fully as possible. Next, press back up, being careful not to lock your knees at the top of the movement. Continue the pressing action for the rest of the set.

The *vertical leg press* is similar in design to the incline leg press except that the platform is directly overhead rather than at an angle. Lie on your back and position yourself so that your hips are directly under the sliding platform. Push up on the platform, release the stops, and lower slowly, bringing your knees toward your chest. Slowly press back up and repeat the exercise for the required number of reps.

Leg Extension

Performed on a special machine, leg extensions are an isolation exercise for shaping and defining the frontal thighs. When performed with light weights, this exercise is an excellent one for people who need to strengthen or rehabilitate weak or injured knees.

Align yourself in the machine so that your back fits comfortably against the seat and the backs of your knees are at the edge of the padded seat. (Most machines will have adjustable seats so that you can set the proper position for your frame.) Hook the insteps of your feet under the padded roller. To begin, slowly straighten your legs, bringing them upward in an arc until they are parallel to the floor. Hold your knees in a tight, locked-out position for two counts, then lower your legs slowly back to the starting position. Repeat.

Tina Plakinger prefers to use a leg extension machine that has a flat bench so that she can lie back to do the exercise. "Performing leg extensions in this position is an excellent way to stress your upper thighs," she says.

Lunge

The lunge isolates the frontal thighs and is performed with a barbell held behind your neck or with two dumbbells, held one along each side of your body. Begin with both legs together. Step forward about two feet with one leg until your frontal thigh is parallel to the floor. Concentrate on getting a good

stretch in your thigh and on keeping your back erect. Your back leg should be as straight as possible. Now push yourself back to the starting position and continue lunging forward on the same leg for the required number of reps. Follow with a set for the other leg.

Leg Curl

The leg curl is a basic exercise for building and shaping the hamstrings. It is performed on a machine designed specifically to isolate these muscles.

Lie face down on the machine's bench. Your lower legs, from knees to feet, should extend off the bench. Hook your ankles under the padded rollers. Flex

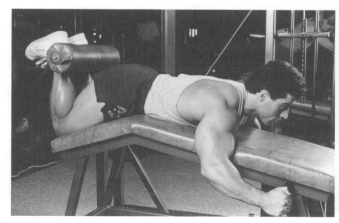

at the knees, bringing your ankles toward your hips in an arc. Lower slowly and repeat.

You can also use the leg curl to work your glutes, with a variation popularized by Ms. Olympia Rachel McLish and used by many bodybuilders, especially women. At the top point of the exercise, when your leg biceps are fully contracted, raise your hips slightly off the bench and squeeze them tightly. With this variation, use a lighter weight than you would with the regular leg curl.

Not all leg curl machines are alike. Some machines feature angled benches for better isolation of the hamstrings, with less emphasis on the glutes. Others are upright units in which you stand, working each leg separately. Standing leg curls place greater stress on the middle and upper hamstrings.

Donkey Calf Raise

Bodybuilders swear by this calf builder and use it as a core exercise in their calf routines because it fully develops the muscles of the lower leg.

With a firm grip on a bench or a rail, lean over so that your torso is parallel to the floor. Place your feet on a four-inch block of wood. Have your training partner ride on your lower back as you raise and lower your heels. Continue the exercise for as many reps as you can.

Donkey calf raises can also be performed on the Nautilus Omni Machine. This version does not require a partner. Simply adjust the middle bar so that when you lean over it your torso is parallel to the floor. Secure the belt around your waist and position your feet on one of the machine's three steps. Lean over, rest your arms across the bar, and raise and lower your heels. Three-time Mr. Olympia Frank Zane uses both versions of the donkey calf raise in his calf building routine.

Standing Calf Raise

Another excellent calf builder is the standing calf raise. Performed on a special machine, this exercise works the gastrocnemius.

With your shoulders fitted comfortably under the pads, raise and lower your heels in a smooth fashion without bouncing at the bottom.

To stimulate the outer and inner heads of your calf muscles, vary your foot position by pointing your toes out for one set and in for another.

Seated Calf Raise

The seated calf raise accentuates the development of the soleus. Sit in the machine and adjust the padded bar so that your knees fit snugly underneath it. Raise your heels as high as you can, then lower them as deeply as you can. Continue the exercise for the required number of reps.

To hit your calves from different angles, point your toes out for one set and in for another.

Toe Press

This exercise works the entire length of the calf and requires a leg press machine. With your legs fully extended and toes on the lower edge of the platform, press back and forth with your feet, striving for maximum stretch in each direction.

Chapter 6

Pectoral Power

Corinna Everson, winning her third Ms. Olympia with her amazing robot routine.

A well-built chest gives shape and width to your upper body—one reason why the chest is such a popular body part to train. To most men, a muscled chest is a prized trait, suggestive of youth, virility, and good looks.

Women can benefit greatly from a few well-chosen bodybuilding exercises too. Bodybuilding recontours the bustline, making it firmer and more attractive.

Athletically, the chest muscles are a major determinant of upper-body strength and power. Most strength routines include plenty of chest work.

Chest Anatomy

The muscles of the chest are the pectoralis major, the broad fan-shaped muscle across the upper chest that assists in rotating and flexing the upper arm, and the pectoralis minor, a thin triangular muscle just under the pectoralis major that moves the shoulder down and forward. Bodybuilders call these muscles the *pecs*.

Juliette Bergman of Rotterdam, Holland.

Two other muscles associated with the chest are the serratus anterior and the intercostals. The serratus anterior is a series of fingerlike muscles running between the ribs and shoulder blades. These muscles assist in shoulder and arm movement. Situated between the ribs, the intercostals are arranged in two layers at right angles to each other. Their function is to lift the ribs to help the diaphragm during inhaling.

Building an Impressive Chest

Your pecs and associated muscle groups respond best when a few basic training principles are applied:

- In the beginning (the first several months of training), use basic exercises: the bench press, incline bench press, and dips. These exercises hit your chest from all angles—front, upper, and lower—and build impressive, overall pectoral mass.
- *Pyramid* your weight, which means starting with a light poundage with ten to twelve reps and progressing to heavier poundage, using six to ten reps. Then perform a final set with a light weight, attempting as many reps as you can. This last set is called a *pump set*. It gives your pectoral muscles additional fiber stimulation.
- Occasionally (once every one or two weeks), use a training method called *forced reps* with the barbell bench press. After you have completed as many reps as you can on a set, have your partner gently pull the bar up as you continue to press. Try to get a few additional reps using this method. Forced reps accelerate your progress and help you overcome plateaus.
- After you've built a substantial amount of mass, add pectoral detail exercises like dumbbell flyes or the pec deck to your routine. Continue to include basic moves like the barbell bench press or dumbbell bench press.

THE EXERCISES

Opposite: Who wouldn't like to look this awesome standing relaxed? Mike Christian is the name.

Bench Press

Tell your out-of-shape friends that you've started working out with weights and then be prepared to answer this question: "How much can you bench press?" The bench press is so well-known that people not involved in iron sports tend to equate bench pressing with weight training.

For all its fame, the bench press is simply a basic barbell exercise designed

to build the pectoral muscles of the chest—a job that it does quite well. It also builds the front part of the shoulders (the deltoids) and the backs of the upper arms (the triceps). Bench pressing is the shortest route to a full, deeply muscled upper body.

To many women, the bench press still carries with it some shreds of machismo, probably because the exercise has always been such an outstanding test of virile strength.

But women should not shy away from this exercise. The bench press works wonders for a woman's bustline, whether it is too large, too small, or just right. You can't change the size of your breasts, except through plastic surgery, weight loss, or weight gain, but you can build up the pectoral muscles, the foundation upon which your breasts lie. For a flat-chested woman, the bench press builds a full, attractive cleavage. For a more full-figured woman, the exercise firms the bustline, giving a more lifted appearance. Bench pressing also helps fight breast sag, a result of gravity's tug on your body as you get older.

To perform this popular chest movement, lie back on a flat bench. Using a grip slightly wider than your shoulders, lift the bar from the rack with help from a training partner and bring it to a straight-arm position above your chest. Slowly lower the bar to your chest, without bouncing at the bottom. Press the bar directly up, concentrating on the force of your pecs. Lower and repeat. Keep your pressing action steady and controlled. Do not arch your back at any time during the exercise. Arching your back puts damaging pressure on the spine.

The incline barbell bench press, performed on a bench angled at about thirty-five degrees, with your head higher than your feet, is a good exercise for triggering muscular gains in your upper pecs. Your lower pecs respond best to decline bench presses, where the bench is sloped at a thirty-five-degree angle and your feet are above head level. On inclines or declines, experiment with different angles to find the one that works best for you. A routine that combines regular bench presses with inclines or declines will build your chest to admirable levels.

Dumbbell Bench Press

To many bodybuilders, the dumbbell bench press is as popular for chest development as the barbell bench press. With dumbbells, you get a greater range of motion, which better strengthens your tendons and ligaments.

To begin, lie back on a flat bench. With your arms extended straight up, hold two dumbbells at right angles to the floor. The palms of your hands should be facing forward. Slowly lower the weights to the sides of your chest, striving for maximum stretch across your pectoral region. Press the dumbbells back up to the starting point and repeat.

You can also perform the dumbbell bench press on an incline bench (a favorite exercise of pro bodyman Jusup Wilcosz) to better work your upper pecs or on a decline bench to better emphasize your lower pecs.

Machine Bench Press

Your pecs can also be worked on a bench press machine. Depending on the machine's design, you may lie on your back and press the bar up or you may sit in an upright position and press the bar forward. Either way, the principles of proper bench pressing still apply. Always keep the bar fully under control and concentrate on strict form.

If you have trouble increasing your weight on barbell bench presses, try a technique called *negatives* once a week on the machine bench press. Using a poundage slightly heavier than normal, have your partner lift the bar for the positive part of the lift. Now lower the bar toward your chest, resisting the gravitational pull as much as possible. Complete one set of about six to ten reps in this manner. Negatives, explained more fully in Chapter 11, promote strength and muscle gains and are useful for breaking through sticking points.

Dips

Back in the fifties, Jack LaLanne thrilled spectators by performing one thousand dips on high parallel bars in just thirty-four minutes. As his feat suggests, dips are superior upper-body strength builders and thus are an excellent move for athletes. Dips also build mass, especially in the lower pecs and serratus anterior.

Pro Bertil Fox, who possesses a massive, well-muscled chest, is an advocate of heavy dips, which he performs with weight hooked to a lifting belt. After you've gained sufficient strength from dips using your own body weight, advance to weighted dips for increased pectoral size and strength.

Hoist yourself up between two parallel bars. With your back arched slightly forward, lower your body as deeply as you can. Then straighten your arms and press your body back up. Lower and repeat.

Dumbbell Flyes

This exercise adds muscular detail to your chest. Lie back on a flat bench. Take a dumbbell in each hand, extend your arms to a position directly over your chest, with palms pointing in. Bend your elbows slightly and slowly lower your arms out to the sides as low as possible. From this position, push the weights back up, following the same path you used to lower them. Continue the exercise for a full set. For upper pec emphasis, try this exercise on an incline bench. (See photos next page.)

Pec Deck

A machine found in most well-equipped gyms, the pec deck is an exceptional device for isolating the inner pectorals, the cleavage area of the chest.

Strap yourself into the seat and place the inner side of your forearms against the pads. Press the pads around, squeezing as you bring your elbows together in front of your chest. At this point, the stress is directly on the inner pecs. Continue moving the pads inward and outward for a full set.

Cable Crossovers

Several weeks before contest time, many bodybuilders add this exercise to their routines because it helps etch in the final chest striations they need for that well-peaked, competition look. For anyone who wants good, all-around muscular tone in the pectoral region, cable crossovers are an excellent exercise.

Stand midway between the high pulleys, with your feet a comfortable distance apart. Take a pulley in each hand, lean forward slightly, and pull the handles down in an arc, crossing them in front of your body. Hold for a moment, flexing your pecs and delts to get full benefit from the contraction. With strict form, return to the starting point and repeat.

Lance Dreher.

Chapter 7

Back Up Your Physique

Tony Pearson.

A body part often difficult to develop is the back. Unlike other muscles, you just can't see your back muscles in action when you train them. As a result, the back often gets shortchanged. Don't let this happen to you. Always try to give your back equal time, because if you build it up, you increase the size of your upper body.

The Anatomy of the Back

The back houses one of the largest muscles in the body—the latissimus dorsi, usually abbreviated to *lats*. The lats arise from the lower portion of your back and fan outward across your rear torso and attach to the inner sides of your arms. The lats have the widest surface area of any muscle on your body. Well-built lats flare at the top and then taper down to the midsection, giving the upper body nice V-shaped symmetry. The resulting contour makes the waist look smaller.

Another major back muscle is the trapezius (usually called the *traps*), a broad, flat, kite-shaped muscle that extends from the base of your neck all the way down to the middle of your back. When fully developed the trapezius beautifully molds the shoulders. The traps and the lats can be partially seen from the front of your body—a good reason for bringing them up to their fullest potential.

Other muscles to concentrate on in back training are the erector spinae, two columns of muscle that flank the spine. Though they span the length of the back, the erectors are most prominent in the lower back, an area called the lumbar region. When the muscles here are weak, low back pain results.

"Oh, My Aching Back"

According to sports training specialist Dr. Michael Yessis, writing in *Muscle and Fitness* (May 1986), low-back pain sends 31 million people to their doctors every year. He lists several reasons for this problem, including poor posture and overweight, which both tend to cause an inward curvature of the spine leading to strain. Fatigue, stress, and improper lifting also cause low back pain. There are many ways to treat low back ailments, from massage to surgery, but it is exercise that offers the best long-term treatment.

In fact, pro bodybuilder Marjo Selin started working out with weights because of a back problem. While in college she began to experience severe back pain, which prompted her to visit doctor after doctor. Pills, bed rest, and surgery were all proposed.

"When I heard 'surgery,' I became frightened," she recalls. "There had to be an alternative. The fourth doctor I saw took X rays and discovered that I had a slight case of scoliosis, lateral curvature of the spine. She told me I had to strengthen my back and abdominal muscles. Shortly afterward I started bodybuilding, and the back pain disappeared."

As Selin learned, exercise can be an excellent prescription for back problems because it strengthens weak muscles.

To strengthen your own back and build it up to admirable levels, you must work it with a variety of bodybuilding exercises that concentrate on the lats, traps, and erectors. Abdominal exercises help prevent low back pain too. They stretch the back and make it more flexible. Developing a strong back is excellent insurance against "oh-my-aching-back" problems later in life.

When performed correctly, the following exercises will help you achieve the results you want, both in appearance and in good health. Be sure to progress gradually and use strict form, without jumping into heavy weights too soon. If you injure your back, you can set your training back for years.

THE EXERCISES

Wide Grip Chins

Pro Tony Pearson's flaring lat spread is certainly testimony to the power of wide grip chins, an exercise he uses regularly in his back routine. This popular, basic exercise does build wide lats.

Take a wide overhand grip on the chinning bar and slowly hoist your body up until your chin is just above the bar. Lower and repeat for as many reps as you can. Later, when you can easily complete fifteen reps, add resistance to the exercise by hooking a weight to your lifting belt.

Lat Pulldown

One of Rachel McLish's favorites, the lat pulldown is a popular, all-purpose back exercise that develops the upper portion of the lats.

Take a wide overhand grip on the lat bar and pull it down behind your neck until it touches your trapezius. In this position, arch your back to achieve maximum contraction in your lats. Slowly return the bar to its starting point and repeat.

For a slightly different feeling, try pulling the bar down in front until it touches your breastbone. This version, called the front lat pulldown, better isolates the lower lats.

Barbell Row

This exercise is one of the most effective mass builders for the back. With your legs slightly bent, lean over so that your torso is flat and parallel to the floor. Take a wide grip on the barbell and pull it directly up toward your midsection. Hold it there for a count or two, as you tense your back muscles. Lower the bar slowly until your arms are completely extended, without touching the weight to the floor. Repeat for additional reps. For a longer range of motion and greater stretch, stand on a wooden board while performing the exercise.

An exercise similar to barbell rowing is *T-bar rowing*, in which you straddle the bar and lift it up at one end, pulling it toward your torso. T-bar rowing builds thickness in the midback, a body part difficult to reach with other exercises.

Dumbbell Row

Using dumbbells in this rowing exercise allows greater isolation of the lats. Bend over so that your back is flat and parallel to the floor. For balance, hold on to a bench with one hand. In the other, hold a dumbbell and extend your arm straight below your shoulder joint so that the weight nearly touches the floor. Pull the dumbbell up into the side of your midsection. Slowly lower the weight back to the starting point. Continue for a complete set and repeat the exercise with the other arm.

Cable Row

Performed on a low pulley machine, this exercise is designed to add both width and thickness to the lats and upper back. Choose a handle with a narrow, parallel grip. From a seated position, lean forward, bend your knees slightly, and straighten your arms. Now, simultaneously sit up and pull the handle into your midsection, using the strength of your lats. At the top of the movement (the contraction) pull your shoulders back and tense your lats for a count or two. Straighten your arms and lean forward, going after a good stretch in your lats. Pull in again and continue the exercise for additional reps.

Pro bodybuilder Albert Beckles, who has one of the most muscular and defined backs in bodybuilding, likes to use a wide lat bar for cable rowing because it hits his lats from a different angle and gives him a better stretch than he gets from conventional handles. Experiment with different grips and handles to find which ones work best for you.

Upright Row

Upright rows are an excellent exercise for the point where your shoulders meet your traps, called the *tie-in*. Stand with your feet a comfortable distance

apart and hold the barbell across your thighs, with your palms toward your body. Pull the barbell slowly up to chin level, keeping your elbows high. With strict form, continue this up/down motion throughout the set.

Upright rows can also be performed either with two dumbbells or with a bar handle attached to a floor pulley.

Shrugs

Shrugs, whether performed with a barbell or with dumbbells, are exceptional trapezius builders. Well-developed traps enhance the look of your shoulders from front and back.

Take a shoulder-wide overhand grip on the bar and hold it across your thighs. With the strength of your traps, lift your shoulders up as high as you can. Rotate them backward, lower to the starting point, and repeat the exercise.

Using dumbbells, hold the weight in each hand, arms straight alongside your body. Lift your shoulders as high as you can in a shrugging motion. At the highest point of the shrug, rotate your shoulders backward and down. Return to the starting point and repeat.

Pullover

The pullover is a multidimensional exercise. Not only does it work your lats, it also works your pecs and triceps.

To begin, select either a short barbell or a cambered bar. Place the barbell on the floor crosswise at the head of a low exercise bench. Lie on your back on the bench. Using a narrow grip with your palms facing the ceiling, slowly pull the weight up from the floor in an arc over your face until it rests just below your chest. Throughout the movement, keep your elbows bent at a ninety-degree angle. Slowly return the weight to the starting point and repeat. If you perform the pullover on a higher bench, your training partner will need to hand you the bar.

You can perform this exercise with a single dumbbell too. Grasp the dumbbell with both hands and extend your arms straight up over your chest. Bend your elbows slightly and lower the weight behind your head. Get a good stretch. Slowly return the dumbbell to the starting position and repeat for additional reps.

The high-tech version of these exercises is performed on the Nautilus Pullover Machine. Using the strength of your lats, you simply press a large bar forward from behind in an arclike path until it touches your waist. Unlike the free weight pullovers, which work several muscles at once, the Nautilus Pullover isolates the lats. For that reason, pro bodybuilder Mike Mentzer likes to start his back routine with the Nautilus Pullover. He feels that it directly stimulates the lats without bringing other muscles into play.

Deadlift

The deadlift is a favorite of Mr. Universe Jeff King, who describes it as "truly the best exercise you can do to build a powerful physique." The deadlift ranks with the squat and the bench press as one of the best and most basic weight training movements for gaining mass, power, and strength. It's debatable whether the deadlift is a back exercise or a leg exercise because it benefits the muscle groups of both.

Begin with the bar on the floor. To start, squat and take an alternate grip on the bar (one hand with an overgrip, the other with an undergrip). Using the

strength of your thighs, slowly stand up, keeping your head up and your back as straight as possible throughout the movement. Now, lower the weight back to the floor by reversing the motion you used to lift it. Repeat for the required number of reps.

Hyperextension

A low-back strengthener, hyperextensions are performed on an apparatus designed specifically for this exercise. Hook your heels under the back of the unit and position yourself so that your torso is free to move up and down. With your hands behind your head, lower your torso toward the floor. Then slowly lift it up until your body forms a straight line.

Some hyperextension units are equipped with a weight stack, which can be connected to your body by a strap you loop around your neck. Attempt added weight only after you have sufficiently strengthened your lower back. If you do not have access to a hyperextension unit, you can perform the exercise on a flat bench or table, with a training partner to secure your legs.

Dynamic
John Terilli.

Chapter 8

Dramatic Delts

Rich Gaspari.

Barn door, doorwaywide, cannonball, melonlike—these are all adjectives bodybuilders use to describe the perfect shoulders . . . broad and full. The shoulder muscles, technically called the *deltoids* or the *delts* for short, respond rapidly to training because they are the most stressed part of your upper body. You use them in bench pressing, in arm work, and in back work, especially when training your trapezius with exercises such as shrugs or upright rows.

Deltoid Anatomy

The deltoid has three sections, the front, medial, and rear heads. Together, they cap the joint where your collarbone and upper arm bone meet. The deltoids work to move the arm in various directions. Strong delts enhance performance in sports, particularly golf, tennis, racquetball, and volleyball, in which arm and shoulder power are critical.

Delt Force

Well-muscled delts create pleasing illusions on your body. By building shoulder mass and width, you make your waist look smaller. Broader shoulders offset hips that are too wide, giving the physique much better symmetry. Delt work also squares off stooped, rounded shoulders to improve posture and overall appearance.

Women get an extra benefit from deltoid exercise. Rather than rely on shoulder pads in dresses and suits, look to bodybuilding as a more natural way to achieve the wide-shoulder look so fashionable right now. If padded shoulders go out of style, you'll be left with a healthy, well-postured look that's always in vogue.

The shoulder area is a delicate joint and can be easily injured, so before working your delts, be sure to warm them up thoroughly with a few light sets of presses or raises.

The key to building impressive shoulders is balanced development of all three heads of the deltoid. To build both mass and shape, use a combination of compound and isolation exercises in your routine. Begin your shoulder routine with compound work such as overhead presses and conclude with isolation exercises (lateral raises, front raises, and bent-over flyes).

THE EXERCISES

Overhead Barbell Press

An excellent muscle builder, the overhead barbell press thoroughly works all three heads of the deltoid.

To prevent unnecessary stress to your lower back, perform this exercise while seated. With assistance from a training partner, take a wide grip on the bar and hold it directly above you. Now lower the bar slowly behind your neck. Then press it back up to an overhead position. Lower again slowly and repeat.

If you press the bar up from the front rather than from behind the neck, you'll place more emphasis on the front delts. Like many champion body-builders, Mr. Olympia Lee Haney uses both front presses and behind-the-neck presses in his deltoid training program.

Dumbbell Shoulder Press

Dumbbell shoulder presses work the front delts. While standing or sitting, hold two dumbbells at shoulder level, palms facing forward. Press both weights upward. Lower and repeat. Keep strict control throughout the move-

ment. This exercise may be performed one arm at a time or in alternating fashion, one arm after the other.

Machine Shoulder Press

This exercise is performed on a weight stack unit designed for shoulder work or on a Nautilus Double Shoulder Machine. It works all three heads of the

deltoid. Sit on the seat with your back to the weight stack and press the bar up to an overhead position, straightening your arms and locking your elbows. Slowly lower the bar and continue the exercise for the required number of reps. To put extra emphasis on your front delts, perform this exercise from a reversed position, facing the machine.

Lateral Raise

This exercise stresses the medial delts. With a dumbbell in each hand, arms alongside your body, lift the weights upward in an arc to a point just above shoulder level. Throughout the movement, keep your elbows slightly bent and your palms facing the floor. Return to the starting point and repeat. Lateral raises can also be performed on a Nautilus Double Shoulder Machine, a favorite exercise of pro Scott Wilson, a man with massive, well-defined delts.

Front Raise

Front raises isolate the front delts. Stand with your feet a comfortable distance apart, and take a shoulder-wide grip on the barbell, positioning it across the top of your thighs. From there, slowly raise the bar up to eye level, keeping your elbows slightly bent. Lower and repeat. Try this exercise with dumbbells, one in each hand. Lift them up to eye level, either together or one after the other, in alternating fashion.

Cable Raise

Cable raises are an excellent exercise for bringing out muscular detail in the front and medial delts. Stand about two feet away from a floor pulley, your left side toward the equipment. Grasp the handle in your right hand and pull the cable across your body and then upward in an arc to a point just above shoulder level. Repeat for a full set and then switch to the other side.

Bent-Over Flyes

Bodybuilders frequently include bent-over flyes in their routines when they want to stimulate growth in their rear delts. From a seated or a standing position, bend forward so that your upper body is parallel to the floor. Hold two dumbbells directly down in front of you with palms pointing inward. Keeping your elbows slightly bent, lift the dumbbells out to the sides as high as you can. Hold them for a moment at the top to feel the contraction. Lower slowly and repeat.

Try this exercise using floor pulleys on the cable machine. Facing the machine, lean over in the same position you used with the dumbbells. Take the right handle in the left hand and the left handle in the right hand so that the cables cross in front of your body. Simultaneously raise and lower the weights in strict fashion for the required number of reps.

Chapter 9

Waist Away

Frank Richard (Britain).

Flat and firm stomach muscles, a well-tapered waistline . . . is this the stuff your dreams are made of? They don't have to be. Taut, fat-free abdominals are possible, as long as you don't overeat, do a moderate amount of aerobic exercise each week to burn fat, and work your abdominals as you would any other body part, progressively and with weights.

Many people have the mistaken notion that doing hundreds of sit-ups every day will rid them of their beer bellies and spare tires. No so. You'll only waste your time, not your tummy. Abdominal muscles (called *abs* for short) respond best to progressive resistance exercise. By adding weight to certain abdominal exercises or by using weight-stacked abdominal machines, you can tone up your abdominals, with less time and fewer repetitions. You need only train your ab muscles two to four times a week, always on nonconsecutive days and with twelve to twenty-five repetitions each set. You'll get excellent results with just a few sets, too.

Ab Anatomy

Like other muscles, the abdominals are a muscle group and therefore must be worked from a variety of angles for maximum shape and tone. Your abdominals are made up of three major muscles, the rectus abdominus, the external obliques, and the internal obliques.

The rectus abdominus is a long, flat muscle that spans the length of the front of your abdomen. It is divided into a left half and a right half by a tendinous seam called the linea alba. The rectus abdominus flexes your trunk.

The external oblique and internal oblique muscles rotate your trunk. The external oblique is a broad, flat muscle covering the sides of your midsection. It runs diagonally from your lats to your rectus abdominus. The internal oblique muscle is a smaller muscle situated just underneath each external oblique.

Midsection Symmetry

Once you begin training your abdominals consistently, you'll be rewarded with a sleek, well-contoured midsection. Strong abdominal muscles put force behind the upper-body power required for the baseball pitch, football pass, tennis serve, and javelin throw. Athletes like gymnasts, wrestlers, and martial artists all need abdominal strength to excel in their sports.

Abdominal exercise helps improve posture and also fights age-related tummy droop. Firm abdominals better support your spine, keep your back properly aligned, and protect your internal organs. In addition, you need strong abs in order to perform squats, deadlifts, and other heavy lifts.

In the exercises that follow, you will not find the familiar straight-leg sit-up. Besides ineffectively working your abs, the sit-up is unsafe. It can strain your lower back. The best exercise to use in place of the sit-up is the abdominal crunch, which works the entire rectus abdominus.

In the beginning, perform these exercises without weight, especially if you haven't exercised your abs in a while. When you can easily complete more than twelve repetitions, add weight and continue to gradually increase poundage for the necessary ab-toning resistance.

With proper diet and regular exercise, you will notice an attractive firmness in your abs in a few short weeks. No longer will you have to hide your abs under bulky shirts or sweaters. These exercises work!

Carolyn Cheshire: England's top pro woman bodybuilder.

THE EXERCISES

Crunch

Three-time Ms. Olympia Corinna Everson calls the crunch "Mr. Old Reliable." A mainstay of stomach workouts, crunches transform soft tummies into rock-hard abs.

To better isolate your abdominals and minimize stress on your lower back, run your legs up a wall or drape your calves across a flat bench. Place your hands behind your head. Using the strength of your ab muscles, lift your upper body from the floor toward your knees. Tense your abs at the top of the movement. Lower and repeat.

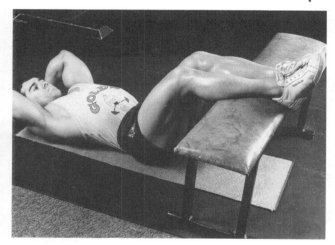 

Intensify this exercise by holding a light dumbbell behind your neck or across your chest as you do the crunch. The added resistance of the weight means extra stimulation for your abdominal muscles.

Another way to stimulate your abs is to perform crunches on a decline bench, with your feet anchored under a bar or strap. The steeper the angle of the bench, the more intense the exercise becomes. Champ Dave Hawk, who unquestionably has one of the most rippled sets of abs in pro bodybuilding, hammers out several sets of decline crunches every other day as part of his ab shaping program.

Machine Crunch

With an abdominal machine, you can perform weighted crunches. Sit in the machine, grasp either handles or a bar, and hook your feet under a padded roller. Next, bring your head toward your knees, concentrating on using just

the strength of your ab muscles, without bringing your back into play. Squeeze your abs tightly at the peak of the contraction. Return to the starting point and repeat.

Reverse Crunch

The reverse crunch is an excellent movement for toning the lower portion of the rectus abdominus. Lie on a mat and grasp the legs of a bench to steady your body. Bend your knees and begin to pull them toward your chest. Now, tuck your knees tightly into your chest, raising your pelvis off the floor. Uncurl your torso and return to the starting point. Repeat. To add muscle-toning resistance to this exercise, wear leg weights, strapped to your ankles.

Nautilus makes a unit called the Hip Machine that simulates the action of a reverse crunch. Set the desired weight, strap yourself across the knees, and lie back on the unit's moveable platform. In a slow, concentrated motion, pull your knees toward your chest. Return to the starting point and repeat.

Knee Raise

Another effective tightening exercise for the lower abs is the knee raise. Sit at the very edge of a bench. For support, hold on to the sides of the bench, placing both hands several inches behind your hips. Angle your torso back slightly. Extend your legs straight out in front, keeping them pressed close together. Now, bend your knees and tuck them into your chest. Return to the starting point and repeat. To intensify the exercise, strap leg weights to your ankles.

Twisting Sit-Up

This exercise tones your obliques and helps you sculpt a small, tight waist.

Use a flat bench for the twisting sit-up. Anchor your feet under the bar or strap. Bend your knees and place your hands behind your head. Curl up, twisting your body so that your elbow meets the opposite knee. Continue this movement for a full set, alternating from side to side.

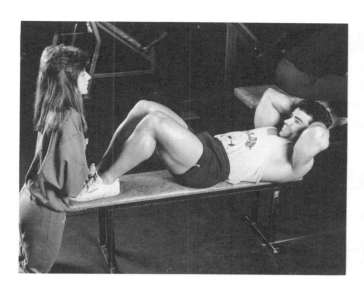
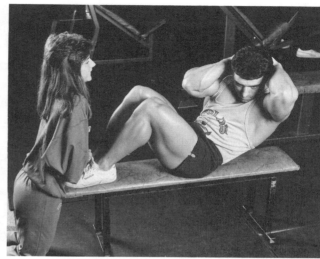

Side Crunch

An excellent waist trimmer, this exercise isolates the oblique muscles. Lie on your side on a flat bench so that from waist up your torso extends off the bench and is free to move up and down. Have your training partner hold your lower body securely on the bench. With hands behind your head, slowly lower and raise your body, bending at the waist. Repeat for the desired number of reps and then continue the exercise on the opposite side.

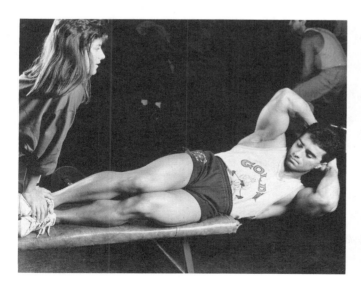
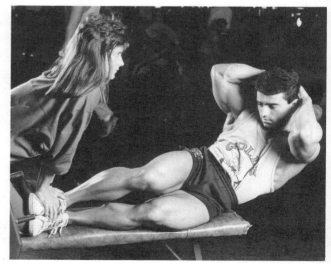

Dumbbell Side Bend

Here's another good waist shaper. Stand with your feet about a foot apart. Hold a dumbbell in each hand, arms alongside your body. Bend your waist first to the right, slowly stretching as far as you can. Return to the starting point and repeat the movement to the left. Continue the right/left action for the rest of the set.

Chapter 10

The Arms You Want

Carla Dunlap.

One of the first questions beginners ask when they start training is "How can I build big arms?" Arms, especially biceps, get a lot of attention in bodybuilding circles. When people ask you if they can feel your muscles, it is your biceps you will flex. A well-developed biceps is truly one of the most dramatic muscles of the upper body.

Arm Anatomy

The biceps has two heads and, like many muscles, varies greatly in shape from person to person. Some people have long biceps, others have short, thick ones. Still others are so genetically gifted that they have been able to easily build an extra peak right on top of their biceps. Strong biceps help you in most sports, especially those in which strength in lifting, climbing, catching, or gripping is required.

Though visually the biceps is the focal point of the arm, it is the triceps muscle that makes up the majority of your arm, about two-thirds of its total muscular mass. The triceps has three sections, the lateral, medial, and long heads. Its main function is to extend the elbow. Strong triceps will help you excel in such activities as racquet sports, basketball, and volleyball.

As you get older, one of the first body parts to show age is the triceps. Without proper exercise, the triceps get flabby, making the skin on your upper arms droop. Firm, strong muscles, achieved by following a balanced arm routine, will help age-proof your body. The more muscled or toned your arms are, the younger you look.

The forearms, the part of your arms between your elbow and wrist, are a body part as stubborn to build as the calves, because the muscle fibers there are so dense. Some bodybuilders do not train them at all, preferring instead to rely on muscular stimulation that carries over from other arm exercises. But Larry Scott, the first Mr. Olympia, is a big believer in forearm training and makes a good case for it. In one of his early training pamphlets, he wrote that his forearms, trained hard over the years, "provide me with a real sense of satisfaction. Probably even more so than the upper arm because they are always in view, even in a short shirt sleeve." Wrestlers, gymnasts, racquet sports players, baseball players, and golfers can all benefit from strong forearms too.

Arm Building Tips

Though forearms may be a little hard to build, your biceps and triceps usually respond quickly to training. In fact, they may be the first body parts to show new muscularity when you begin to bodybuild. The following tips will help you get the most from your arm training:

Opposite:
Jeff Smullen.

103

John Terilli,
Lee Haney and
Rocky DeFerro.

- The triceps is a large multiple muscle that often requires extra work, so begin your arm routine with triceps exercises, when your energy level is still fairly high.
- With triceps exercises, always lock your elbows out at the end of the movement for maximum stress on the muscle.
- Begin your biceps exercises with one or two basic movements such as the barbell curl or the dumbbell curl and finish off with an isolation exercise such as the cable curl. "This system hits your biceps from all angles and develops both mass and shape," says NPC Collegiate National Champ Todd King, one of bodybuilding's most promising newcomers.
- Flex your biceps hard at the top of all curling exercises for extra stress on the muscle.
- In all arm work, use ultrastrict form, accentuating the negative portion of the exercise.
- Arm muscles adapt easily to sameness. Many bodybuilding champs change their arm workouts frequently to spark new muscle growth. For a change of pace, try *supersetting* arm work, in which you perform a biceps exercise followed immediately, without stopping, by a triceps exercise. *Descending sets*, in which you start with a heavy weight and work down to lighter ones, are another good way to stimulate muscular gains in your arms. Both techniques are covered more fully in the next chapter.

THE EXERCISES

Barbell Curl

The barbell curl is unsurpassed for building biceps mass and overall arm strength. To begin, take an undergrip on the bar, with your hands spaced a bit wider than shoulder width. Hold the bar across your thighs and stand with your feet a comfortable distance apart. Now bend your arms at the elbows and raise the bar in an arc to the top of your chest. Tense your biceps in this contracted position. During the lift, be sure to keep your elbows and upper arms pressed close against the sides of your body. Do not let your upper body sway back as you lift. With strict control, lower the bar slowly back to the starting point and repeat.

   Some bodybuilders prefer to use a cambered bar for curling because it gives a better grip. For variety, pro Rich Gaspari uses both a cambered and a straight bar, alternating between the two when working his arms.

Preacher Curl

Preacher curls (also called Scott curls) emphasize the lower section of the biceps. To do preacher curls, select a barbell a bit lighter than you would normally use for the standard curl. Take the barbell and lean over the preacher bench (a padded apparatus that holds the elbows in place) so that your underarms fit below the upper edge of the bench. With your arms parallel to each other, slowly curl the bar upward to a point near chin level. Pause for a moment to contract your biceps at the peak of the exercise. With concentrated control, lower the bar and repeat for the required number of reps.

Dumbbell Curl

The dumbbell curl, an exercise with many variations, is another excellent biceps builder. To begin, stand with your feet a comfortable distance apart. With arms at your sides, hold a dumbbell in each hand, palms facing your body. At the beginning of the curl, rotate your wrist so that your palms now face front. This movement is called supination. It's an extra arm-building factor that you get with dumbbell curls. With strict form, curl the weights up toward your chest. Now lower slowly and repeat. This exercise may be done in alternating fashion too, one arm after another, curling up and down in a rhythmic, seesaw motion.

Arnold Schwarzenegger's favorite arm exercise is the incline dumbbell curl. Performed on a slanted bench, this exercise works the full length of the biceps, with extra emphasis placed on the outer head.

Begin with your arms extended directly down from your shoulders and your palms facing the bench. Rotate your wrists, curl the dumbbells up toward your shoulders, and tense your biceps at the top of the exercise. Slowly lower the weights back to the starting point. For an even deeper effect on the outer head of your biceps, angle your arms out from your sides as you curl up.

Concentration Curl

The concentration curl is an exercise valued as a way to achieve that highly sought-after biceps peak.

Sit on a bench, take a dumbbell in one hand, and brace your arm by placing your elbow against your inner thigh. Rest your free hand on your other thigh. From a straight arm position, slowly bend your elbow and curl the weight up toward your shoulder. Hold this position for a count or two while tensing your biceps hard at the top of the movement. Slowly lower the weight back to the starting point and repeat. Be sure to work each arm with an equal number of reps.

Cable Curl

Used often by Mr. Olympia Lee Haney in his arm routine, the cable curl is a muscle-shaping exercise, excellent for chiseling the biceps into superb condition.

Take a floor pulley with one hand, palm facing forward and arm straight against your side. Keeping an erect posture, pull the handle up toward your shoulder in an arc. Lower and repeat. At the conclusion of the set, work the other arm with an equal number of reps.

Machine Curl

This exercise is performed on a machine that simulates free weight curling exercises. To begin, brace your arms against the padded, angled surface of the machine and take hold of the handles with your palms facing up. Now pull the handles toward your chin in an arc. Lower slowly and repeat. On most machines, you have the option of working your biceps one at a time or together.

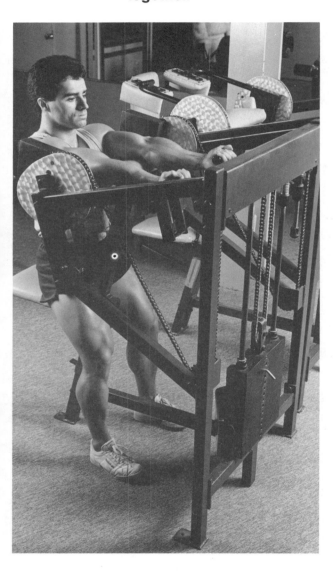 

Reverse Curl

This exercise helps develop the forearm, a muscle group that must be worked like the calves—hard, heavy, and with a rep range of fifteen to twenty. "You just can't work them too much," says forearm exercise advocate Larry Scott.

Take a shoulder-wide, overhand grip on the barbell. Begin with your arms straight and the bar resting across your thighs. Curl up with the barbell, keeping your wrists straight and your elbows and upper arms braced against your body. Lower slowly and repeat.

Barbell Wrist Curl

The barbell wrist curl is another popular forearm exercise. When performed with palms up, wrist curls accentuate the flexors, located on the palm side of the forearm; performed with palms down, they accentuate the extensors, located on the back of the forearm.

From a seated position with your arms resting on your knees, curl the bar up in a small arc, moving just your wrists. Lower the bar slowly, maintaining strict form, and repeat for the required number of reps.

Bench Dips

Bench dips are effective for building strength and size in the triceps. To begin, place two flat benches parallel to each other, about as far apart as the length of your legs. With your back to one of the benches, grasp its edge behind you, making sure that your forearms and fingers are pointing forward. Bridge the two benches with your body by extending your legs across to the other bench and placing your feet upon it. Slowly bend your elbows to lower your hips close to the floor. Push yourself back up by straightening your arms. Repeat. To add resistance to this exercise, place a plate on your lap.

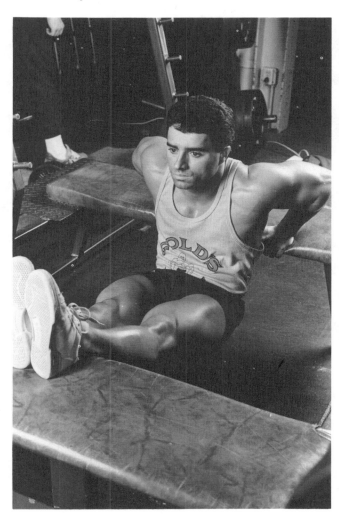 

Lying Triceps Extension

This exercise is a basic, all-purpose triceps builder, effective for triggering mass and strength gains. Take a narrow reverse grip on a cambered or straight bar and lie back on a flat bench. Begin with your arms extended straight up in front of you. Without moving your upper arms, bend your elbows, letting the bar travel back in an arc just to your forehead. At this point, your upper arms should be vertical and parallel to each other. Then reverse the motion, returning the bar to the starting point. Continue the exercise for the required number of reps. Lou Ferrigno suggests performing this exercise on a decline bench angled at about twenty degrees for a deeper, more thorough triceps workout.

Close Grip Bench Press

This exercise is performed like the barbell bench press, except that you take a very narrow overgrip, as its name indicates. By gripping the bar with your hands close together, you shift primary emphasis from the pecs to the triceps.

Lie back on a flat bench. Begin as you would with the bench press by lifting the bar from the rack and bringing it to a position above your chest, with your arms fully extended. Slowly lower the bar to your chest and then press back up until your elbows are tightly locked out. As you continue the exercise, concentrate on using the force of your triceps muscles.

A variation on this exercise is the reverse grip bench press, another excellent triceps builder. Take a shoulder-wide undergrip on the bar. Using strict bench press form, press up from your abdominals. Lower and repeat.

Pulley Pushdown

Performed on a lat machine or similar apparatus, pulley pushdowns work the entire length of the triceps, with particular stress on the outer head. The standard handle for this exercise is a short, V-shaped bar.

Face the weight stack and take a narrow overgrip on the bar. Begin with your elbows fully bent and your upper arms braced against your sides. With the strength of your triceps, press the bar down until your arms are straight and your elbows fully locked out. Slowly let the bar return to the starting point and repeat.

Dumbbell Triceps Extension

This exercise emphasizes the inner and middle heads of the triceps. With both hands, grasp a dumbbell and hold it behind your head. Your elbows should point toward the ceiling and your upper arms should be pressed close to your head. Raise the weight overhead, straightening your arms and locking your elbows. Then slowly lower the dumbbell back to the starting point and repeat for additional reps. The triceps extension may also be performed one arm at a time.

Chapter 11

Getting into a Routine

Ellen Van Maris.

Seminar after seminar, people ask pro bodybuilders these questions: "How many reps, how many sets should I do? What poundage should I use, heavy weights or light weights? How many times a week should I work out?"

Although there are no pat answers to these questions, certain aspects of reps and sets have been scientifically researched. Studies as far back as the forties theorized that heavy weights and low repetitions are best for building strength and light weights and high repetitions are best for developing endurance. In the sixties, a study determined that the right combination for building strength was three sets of six reps. And today, a new study says three sets of twenty reps may be the best way to make strength gains. The debate continues!

Routines must be individual, based on your age, on your level of fitness, and on the amount of time you can reasonably spend in the gym. To guide you on structuring your own workouts, here are several routines, each one created to meet certain needs. You can follow these routines exactly as written or modify them for your age, your schedule, or the type of equipment available to you.

Be sure to keep a training log too, in which you record your routine, the number of reps and sets you do, and the amount of weight you lift. As soon as your second workout, your strength will be greater, signaling that your muscles have already begun to respond. This immediate feedback is an excellent motivator. Charting your workout also encourages progressive training, with ever-increasing intensity.

Before you begin any exercise routine, it's a good idea to have a medical checkup by a doctor knowledgeable in sports medicine.

Three Days a Week

In their zeal to develop the same physiques they see on muscle magazine covers, aspiring bodybuilders often think they need to copy the pros' brutal six-day-a-week, multiple-set routines featured in the magazines.

Workout sessions three times a week, forty-five to sixty minutes each, result in excellent progress. Set your workout schedule up so that you train on nonconsecutive days—for instance on Monday, Wednesday, and Friday, or on Tuesday, Thursday, and Saturday. The muscles you worked need at least one day for rest and repair before you train them again. This process is called recuperation. It is an important element of muscular growth.

Conditioning Routine

This routine is designed for children age twelve or younger who want to learn the fundamentals of weight training. It is also appropriate for out-of-shape adults who have never done much exercise before. The routine includes exercises that use one's own body weight as the resistance necessary for conditioning the muscles. These exercises get your body ready for heavier training later on. In this routine, you also begin to learn proper lifting techniques by using an unloaded barbell. Repetitions are kept high so that you spend time learning and practicing perfect form. Perform this routine three times a week on nonconsecutive days.

Exercises	Reps	Sets
Lunge (no weight)	10–15 each leg	1–2
Wide Grip Chins	Up to 15	1–2
Crunch	10–15	1–2
Beginner's Squat	10–15	1–2
Bench Press	10–15	1–2
Overhead Barbell Press	10–15	1–2

Beginner's Routine

After you've mastered basic lifting techniques and developed adequate tone and strength, you're ready to increase your workload with additional exercises that use a moderate amount of weight—enough so that you can perform at least twelve to fifteen reps without too much strain. If you're under age sixteen, keep your poundage light and your repetitions high. Your bones have not yet stopped growing, and handling heavy poundage can damage your skeletal structure.

Exercises	Reps	Sets
Squat	10–15	1–2
Leg Curl	10–15	1–2
Bench Press	10–15	1–2
Overhead Barbell Press	10–15	1–2
Barbell Row	10–15	1–2
Hyperextension	10–15	1–2
Triceps Extension	10–15	1–2
Barbell Curl	10–15	1–2
Calf Raise	10–15	1–2
Crunch	10–15	1–2

In most bodybuilding routines, the largest muscle groups are worked first, when your energy level is at its peak.

Take short rests between sets to let your muscles recover. A good rule of thumb is to rest one minute between sets. Resting any longer than a minute lets your body cool down too much, making muscles, joints, and connective tissue more susceptible to injury.

Continue to work out three times a week on nonconsecutive days.

Intermediate Routine

After a few months on the beginner's routine, you should be ready to tackle heavier weights, using the *pyramid system*, in which you increase your poundage each set while decreasing your reps.

Establish your initial poundage by attempting six to twelve repetitions per set using strict form. If you cannot handle as many as six, the weight is too heavy. On the other hand, if you can complete twelve or more repetitions without exertion, the weight is too light.

Jusup Wilcosz of
West Germany.

Consider dividing your workouts into heavy, medium, and light days. On your heavy day, strive for heavy poundage on each set, with a rep scheme of ten on the first set, eight on the second, and six on the third. On your medium day, your reps would be twelve, ten, and eight, with moderate loads; and the light day would be devoted to light weights, using the rep scheme of fifteen, twelve, and ten. These sharp periodic increases trigger consistent gains.

A note of caution: In bodybuilding, you compete against your last lifts, not against the person at the next bench who is pressing much heavier weights than you. Progress at your own rate. Strength and muscular gains occur steadily week after week, month after month. There's plenty of time.

Exercises	Reps	Sets
Squat or Leg Press	6–15	2–3
Leg Curl	6–15	2–3
Deadlift	6–15	2–3
Bench Press	6–15	2–3
Dips	6–15	2–3
Wide Grip Chins (with weight)	6–15	2–3
Cable Row	6–15	2–3
Front Overhead Barbell Press	6–15	2–3
Shrugs	6–15	2–3
Lying Triceps Extension	6–15	2–3
Barbell Curl	6–15	2–3
Donkey Calf Raise	12–25	2–3
Machine Crunch	12–25	2

Advanced Bodybuilding

As you gain more experience, go on to compete in bodybuilding contests, or want to fine-tune the muscular shape you've gained from your three-day-a-week routine, consider working out on a more advanced routine. Advanced routines split the body up for each training session but still allow adequate recuperation time for the muscles worked.

Four-Day Split

On a four-day split, you train your lower body on Monday, your upper body on Tuesday, skip a day, then repeat the pattern on Thursday and Friday. One variation is to train every other day, alternating lower-body workouts with upper-body workouts. Another way to split the body is to work on chest, back, and arms one day, and legs, shoulders, and abdominals the next.

The four-day split is a good routine for dieters. By adding another training day to your week, you increase your weekly caloric expenditure. Continue to pyramid your poundages.

MONDAY / THURSDAY

Exercises	Reps	Sets
Squat or Leg Press	6–12	3–4
Leg Extension	6–12	3
Hack Squat	6–12	3
Leg Curl	6–12	3
Calf Raise	12–25	2–3
Toe Press	12–25	2–3
Knee Raise	6–12	2–3
Crunch	12–25	2–3

TUESDAY / FRIDAY

Exercises	Reps	Sets
Bench Press	6–12	3–4
Incline Bench Press (with barbells or dumbbells)	6–12	3
Lat Pulldown	6–12	3
Cable Row	6–12	3
Overhead Barbell Press	6–12	3–4
Lateral or Front Raise	6–12	3
Reverse Grip Bench Press	6–12	3
Pulley Pushdown	6–12	3
Preacher Curl	6–12	3
Incline Dumbbell Curl	6–12	3

Six-Day Split Routine

On a typical six-day split routine, you work your chest and back on Monday, shoulders and arms on Tuesday, legs and abdominals on Wednesday, rest a day, and then start the cycle over again.

Six-day splits should be followed only by individuals who have been training for a few years or who are preparing for a bodybuilding competition. A routine like this can be very taxing, mentally and physically, so before you attempt it, be sure that you're committed to doing six workouts a week in the gym.

This routine splits the body into three parts, with each part worked on a separate day. The three workouts are punctuated by a day of rest to give your body adequate recuperative time before repeating the cycle.

DAY ONE—CHEST AND BACK

Exercises	Reps	Sets
Bench Press	6–12	4–5
Incline or Decline Bench Press	6–12	4–5
Pec Deck or Cable Crossovers	6–12	4–5
Lat Pulldown	6–12	4–5
Cable Row	6–12	4–5
Upright Row	6–12	4–5

DAY TWO—LEGS AND ABS

Exercises	Reps	Sets
Leg Press	6–12	4–5
Hack Squat	6–12	4–5
Leg Extension	6–12	4–5
Leg Curl	6–12	4–5
Donkey Calf Raise	12–25	3–4
Seated Calf Raise	12–25	3–4
Crunch	12–25	3–4
Twisting Sit-Up	12–25	3–4
Knee Raise	12–15	3–4

DAY THREE—SHOULDERS AND ARMS

Exercises	Reps	Sets
Machine Shoulder Press	6–12	4–5
Dumbbell Shoulder Press	6–12	4–5
Bent-Over Flyes	6–12	4–5
Close Grip Bench Press	6–12	4–5
Pulley Pushdown	6–12	4–5
Machine Curl	6–12	4–5
Cable Curl	6–12	4–5
Reverse Curl	12–15	4–5

On day four—rest.

Overtraining

For novice bodybuilders, split routines can lead to a condition called *over-training*, caused by doing too much work too soon. Symptoms of overtraining include strength decreases, fatigue, weight loss, chronic pain in muscles and joints, digestive problems, and depression. One or more of these symptoms is a sign you have overtrained. The best way to avoid this condition is by not jumping prematurely into advanced routines. Wait until you have made significant progress working out just three times a week.

The most important point about your training is to maintain balance in your life. That means making time for friends, family, sports, school, career, and other activities. You risk burnout—physical and mental—if you spend too much time working out.

Changing Your Routine

Your body needs lots of variety. To keep making muscle, you have to regularly change your routines. But how often? "Some [bodybuilders] can do the same routine for months without a change and others need a change weekly," Lou Ferrigno said in *Muscle Mag International*, "but a good medium is every four to six weeks."

Before you change, give a routine or an exercise enough time so that you can fairly assess how well you are gaining on it, in both strength and size. Then make the necessary adjustments.

Gary Strydom.

125

Double Strength Training

As long as weight training has been around, lifters, bodybuilders, and other athletes have been experimenting with new ways to boost muscular size and strength. Here are several proven training techniques that when used correctly promise to give you satisfying results.

FAILURE AND FORCED REPS. When you push yourself so hard that you can't finish the last rep of a set, you've trained to *failure*. To break past that barrier, have your training partner assist you with a few more reps by gently lifting the bar as you continue to push. These reps are called *forced reps*. Popularized by Mike Mentzer in his "Heavy Duty" training system, forced reps give you the edge you need to overcome plateaus or sticking points in certain exercises. For best results, use them only occasionally in your workouts, no more than once a week.

NEGATIVES. Negative training is a well-accepted method of building size and strength, especially in muscles that are weak and lag in development. There are two types of negative training: negative-only exercise and negative-accentuated training.

With *negative-only* exercise, your partner raises the weight for you. Then, on your own power, you lower the weight slowly, resisting its gravitational momentum.

Negative-accentuated training does not require a training partner. You lift the weight with two legs or two arms, depending on the exercise, and then lower it with one. A good exercise to try this technique on is the leg curl. With both ankles under the padded roller, curl up, then slide one foot off, and slowly lower the weight back to the starting position. Then repeat for the other leg.

Other exercises that lend themselves well to negative work are barbell curls, chins, lateral and front raises, and some machine exercises. Do negatives as a whole set or as a few reps at the end of a set. As with forced reps, perform negatives no more than once a week.

SUPERSETTING. Supersets spark muscle growth. Generally, they combine two different exercises, performed without rest in between. There are several ways to superset exercises:

- Same muscle: On each set, you work the same muscle but use a different exercise. For example, train your triceps with lying extensions followed immediately by pulley pushdowns. Many bodybuilders use *trisets*, supersets consisting of three different exercises, or *giant sets* made up of four (sometimes five) different exercises.

- Opposing muscles: Here, you simply work antagonistic muscles, such as triceps and biceps or quadriceps and hamstrings, one muscle right after the other with little rest in between.
- Push-pull: This superset alternates pushing and pulling exercises—for instance, overhead presses with upright rowing. Mr. Olympia Lee Haney trains with the push-pull system.

PRE-EXHAUSTION. Similar to supersetting, pre-exhaustion means attacking a certain muscle with an isolation exercise first, followed immediately by a compound exercise. In many compound exercises, you're handicapped by *weak link* muscles that give out early in the set, limiting development of larger, stronger muscle groups. Pre-exhaustion works those muscle groups harder than ever.

Take the deltoids. The overhead press is one of the best exercises for building the shoulders. But because your triceps tire out early, your deltoids miss out on the full benefit of the exercise. To get around this, isolate your delts first with an exercise that does not directly involve the triceps, like lateral raises with dumbbells. Go to failure and then right into the overhead press. The lateral raises pre-exhaust your delts, making your triceps temporarily stronger in the overhead press so that you can complete the exercise without limitations. Your deltoids get maximum stimulation.

For other body parts, pre-exhaust combinations to try are dumbbell flyes and bench presses (chest), leg extensions and squats (thighs), shrugs and bent-over rows (back), crunches and knee raises (abs), standing calf raises and rope jumping (calves), concentration curls and barbell curls (biceps), and pulley pushdowns and close-grip bench press (triceps).

REST-PAUSE. Heavy weights produce the greatest muscular gains. With rest-pause, you can handle heavier weights than you're accustomed to and get the muscle-building benefits of heavy work.

Using a heavier-than-normal poundage, perform a few reps and rest for about fifteen seconds. Perform a few more reps, rest fifteen seconds, and follow up with two to three more reps. Rest-pause training is intense, so use it on just one muscle group, no more than once a week.

DESCENDING SETS. Another way to stimulate gains with heavy poundage is to use descending sets—the exact opposite of pyramiding. Start with as heavy a weight as you can lift for six to eight reps. Then go on to the next-lighter weight for as many reps as you can, continuing with a lighter weight each set. The muscles you work with descending sets must be thoroughly warmed up before you start.

Muscle Soreness

An extra-hard workout, new exercises, a return to training after a layoff—these are all conditions that can cause stiffening aches in your muscles a day or two after training. No one yet knows the real reason behind muscle soreness, but there are some theories.

One theory holds that weight training cuts blood flow to your muscles, limiting the muscles' ability to wash out waste products that build up during exercise. The accumulation of waste products excites nerve endings, which translate the feeling as pain. Another theory holds that soreness is caused by uncontrollable contractions, called *spasms*, in muscles. Still other evidence suggests that exercise causes tears in muscle tissue. The muscle tissue then swells, triggering nerve endings, which in turn signal pain.

Regardless of the true cause of muscle soreness, you can help prevent it by adequate warmups before training. Massage, heat, sports creams, whirlpools, and rest are ways to relieve muscle soreness whenever you do get it. If muscular soreness lasts longer than a week, see your doctor. The pain may signal a more serious injury.

Fat Burners

Along with bodybuilding, you need aerobic exercise. Aerobic exercise strengthens your heart and makes your lungs more efficient. To work, the aerobic activity must elevate your pulse to approximately 80 percent of your maximum heart rate (220 minus your age) and keep it there for twenty minutes or longer.

Aerobic exercise is a fat burner. It boosts the production of enzymes that change fat to energy. So the more fat-burning enzymes you have, the better your body burns its stored fat, during exercise and at rest.

Look for ways to include aerobics in your fitness program. Well-equipped gyms have aerobic equipment such as stationary bicycles, rebounders, treadmills, rowing machines, and cross-country ski machines. Most of this equipment is affordable and thus appropriate for home use too. Several companies manufacture high-tech bicycles, rowers, and treadmills that give you digital readouts with information such as calories burned per hour, elapsed time, and the terrain to be covered. One rower in particular even has sound effects—the starter's gun and crowd cheering!

Although aerobic exercise is the best way to tune up your cardiovascular system, some forms can be damaging to joints, bones, and muscles, particularly high-impact exercise like running and aerobic dancing. Both tend to jar the body, potentially causing injury. The trend in aerobics is now toward "soft" exercise, which is gentler to the body because it does not involve

Opposite: Even relaxed, multi–Mr. Olympia Lee Haney looks unbeatable.

129

bouncing. Examples include walking, biking, swimming, rowing, and cross-country skiing. Many aerobic dance studios now offer *low-impact aerobics*, made up of moves that keep one foot on the ground at all times and use the upper body in the routines just as much as the legs.

For peak aerobic conditioning, work out for thirty to forty-five minutes each session at least three times a week. If you bodybuild and do aerobics on the same day, allow several hours of rest between the two workouts. Adequate rest will keep your energy level high for both types of training. Or, alternate your aerobic days with your bodybuilding days.

Dumbbell curls
as performed by
Gary Leonard.

Opposite:
Penny Price.

Chapter 12

Peak Athletics

Ernie Santiago (Hawaii).

When Detroit Tigers catcher Lance Parrish showed up at spring training camp in 1982, he weighed 245 pounds, much heavier than his assigned reporting weight of 220. Though the added bulk was pure weight-trained muscle, Parrish was in trouble. He was "overweight" and subject to a fine.

On top of that, the team manager was furious, for Parrish had shown great promise as a home run hitter, and now the question was whether he could even swing a bat with all that extra beef. Parrish was ordered to stop pumping iron and get himself back down to the right size.

He ignored those orders, continued to lift, and hit thirty-two home runs that season, setting a new record for American League catchers. His next season was equally impressive. He hit twenty-seven homers and scored 114 RBI. To what did he credit this tremendous home run power? Weight training, of course. But there's more. Parrish said that the weights had also improved his confidence, stamina, and overall health. (These details are taken from an article by Scott Ostler, carried in 1984 by the LA Times–Washington Post News Service.)

The sports world is full of success stories like this one, in which weight training gave athletes the winning edge. "In athletics, weight training is a necessary ingredient," says Mike Carter of the National Strength and Conditioning Association (NSCA). "No matter what the sport, it helps determine both individual and team success."

As an athlete, the stronger you are the more successful you will be in sports. Muscular strength gives you speed, power, and stamina. It reduces your chances of injury and extends your playing lifetime. Whether you're a linebacker or a weekend golfer, you can improve your game considerably by learning how to train for strength.

Getting Strong

The best way to begin a strength training program is to enlist the help of a qualified strength coach (many athletic teams have them) or a trainer who can assess the physical requirements of your sport and develop a routine for you that will maximize your performance. A strength coach or trainer can observe you, either in the game or on film, analyze your performance, and formulate a program to correct your specific weaknesses.

Strength training routines are built upon certain *core* lifts, exercises designed to develop the body's power zone—the area that extends from the hips to the lower back to the shoulder girdle. Build up these areas and you strengthen your ability to jump, run, throw, stop and start, and so on. The core lifts a coach designates for a team vary according to the sport and to the athletes' level of ability and experience. For athletes just beginning to

133

strength train, core exercises are usually the squat, power clean, deadlift, and bench press.

The squat develops overall body strength; the power clean, explosive power; and the deadlift, lower back and hip strength. The bench press increases upper-body strength, which is especially important for athletes such as defensive linemen, shot putters, pitchers, or javelin throwers, who must exert great upper-body force in their sports. Upper-body strength has also been found to be essential for sprinters and runners. The faster they can move their arms, the faster they run.

In addition to the core exercises, a strength training routine includes auxiliary lifts—additional weight training exercises designed to strengthen an athlete's weaker muscles. A strength coach or trainer can be very helpful in identifying the appropriate auxiliary exercises for your sport and your level of ability.

Robby Robinson and John Brown.

Here is a list of auxiliary exercises, catalogued by sport, that are apt to be included (along with core exercises) in an athlete's strength training program. The exercises can be performed with free weights or with machines.

BASEBALL
Incline Bench Press
Dumbbell Flyes
Upright Row
Pullover
Front Raise
Triceps Extension
Curl
Twisting Sit-Up

BASKETBALL
Leg Extension
Leg Curl
Upright Row
Lat Pulldown
Pullover
Lateral Raise
Triceps Extension
Curl
Donkey Calf Raise
Crunch

BICYCLING
Leg Press
Leg Curl
Lat Pulldown
Hyperextension
Shrug
Pulley Pushdown
Curl
Wrist Curl
Donkey Calf Raise
Crunch

BOWLING
Lunge
Leg Extension
Cable Row
Hyperextension
Pulley Pushdown
Curl
Wrist Curl
Crunch

FOOTBALL
Leg Press
Leg Curl
Overhead Barbell Press
Shrug
Hyperextension
Close Grip Bench Press
Curl
Twisting Sit-Up

GOLF
Hack Squat
Incline Bench Press
Dip
Upright Row
Lateral Raise
Pulley Pushdown
Curl
Twisting Sit-Up

GYMNASTICS

Leg Extension
Leg Curl
Incline Press
Dip
Overhead Barbell Press
Lateral Raise
Cable Row
Hyperextension
Pulley Pushdown
Curl
Crunch

HOCKEY

Leg Press
Leg Extension
Leg Curl
Incline Bench Press
Dip
Upright Row
Shrug
Lat Pulldown
Triceps Extension
Curl
Twisting Sit-Up

RACQUET SPORTS

Hack Squat
Leg Curl
Dumbbell Shoulder Press
Incline Bench Press
Upright Row
Shrug
Lateral Raise
Triceps Extension
Curl
Reverse Curl
Twisting Sit-Up

ROWING

Hack Squat
Dip
Upright Row
Cable Row
Hyperextension
Triceps Extension
Curl
Crunch

SKIING

Leg Press or Lunge
Leg Extension
Leg Curl
Incline Bench Press
Dip
Lat Pulldown
Shrug
Triceps Extension
Curl
Twisting Sit-Up

SOCCER

Hack Squat
Leg Extension
Incline Bench Press
Dip
Bent-Over Row
Pullover
Close Grip Bench Press
Curl
Twisting Sit-Up

Opposite:
Rich Gaspari.

SWIMMING
Hack Squat
Leg Extension
Leg Curl
Dip
Cable Row
Pullover
Dumbbell Shoulder Press
Front Raise
Shrug
Pulley Pushdown
Curl
Knee Raise

DISCUS, SHOT PUT
Leg Extension
Incline Bench Press
Overhead Barbell Press
Lat Pulldown
Pulley Pushdown
Curl
Twisting Sit-Up

DISTANCE RUNNING
Leg Press
Leg Curl
Upright Row
Pullover
Pulley Pushdown
Curl
Donkey Calf Raise
Twisting Sit-Up

HIGH JUMP
Hack Squat
Leg Extension
Leg Curl
Dip
Pulley Pushdown
Curl
Toe Press
Crunch

JAVELIN
Leg Extension
Leg Curl
Incline Bench Press
Lat Pulldown
Upright Row
Triceps Extension
Toe Press
Crunch

LONG JUMP
Hack Squat
Lunge
Incline Bench Press
Pullover
Pulley Pushdown
Curl
Donkey Calf Raise
Knee Raise

138

POLE VAULT
Leg Press
Leg Curl
Dip
Upright Row
Front Raise
Pullover
Hyperextension
Triceps Extension
Curl
Donkey Calf Raise
Twisting Sit-Up

SPRINTING
Hack Squat
Lunge
Leg Curl
Incline Bench Press
Hyperextension
Triceps Extension
Curl
Toe Press
Crunch

VOLLEYBALL
Hack Squat
Leg Curl
Incline Bench Press
Front Press
Triceps Extension
Curl
Reverse Curl
Donkey Calf Raise
Knee Raise

WRESTLING
Leg Extension
Leg Curl
Dip
Dumbbell Shoulder Press
Bent-Over Row
Hyperextension
Triceps Extension
Twisting Sit-Up

Strength Builders

Athletes training for strength generally work out three times a week on nonconsecutive days, with their routines structured on a heavy-medium-light system to assure steady progress.

Strength coaches regularly employ certain weight training techniques to encourage strength gains, including:

CYCLING. Excellent gains come from *cycling*, a method of training organized in periods, or *cycles*, each characterized by variations in rep schemes, sets, and poundage. The athlete gradually increases intensity in each cycle, usually progressing from low-intensity work with light weights and high repetitions to high-intensity work with heavy weights and low reps.

Cycling helps an athlete overcome training plateaus and break through sticking points. A typical cycling program may last anywhere from eight to sixteen weeks.

Cycling is a Soviet concept and has been a part of strength training programs in the United States since the seventies.

FORCED REPS. In strength training, forced reps are used to build extra strength and power. To do them, train to failure on a set and then have your partner or coach help you complete a few additional reps.

LIMITED-RANGE LIFTS. Besides increasing muscular strength, limited-range lifts strengthen ligaments and tendons. Limited-range lifts are used chiefly with exercises like the bench press and squat. They require a power rack—a piece of equipment with adjustable safety pins positioned at certain heights to allow lifting through a set range of motion.

Al Roy shows the type of body that can be achieved with only a few months of training.

To perform this technique using the bench press, for example, complete two to three sets of bench presses. Then insert the pins in both sides of the rack so that the bar is supported at a point about midway between your chest and full lockout. Load the bar with a poundage slightly heavier than you are accustomed to lifting. Now press the bar up to lockout and back, repeating the lift for as many reps as you can. Your range of motion is about half that of a regular bench press. On your next set, raise the pin adjustment so that the bar is supported just above the midway mark. Again press up to lockout and back. Repeat for as many reps as you can manage. Your range of motion will be about one-third that of a regular bench press.

SINGLES. This technique is used primarily with squats, bench presses, and deadlifts. Rest for about a minute after you have completed your last heavy set. Now load the bar with a heavy weight, one you know you can barely force one or two reps from. With assistance from your training partner, attempt one rep only.

NEGATIVES. Negative training is a well-accepted method of building strength, especially in weaker body parts. Use both types of negative training in your program: negative-only exercise and negative-accentuated training. Both methods are explained in Chapter 11.

Forced reps, limited-range lifts, singles, and negatives should be used sparingly, no more than once every one to two weeks. When overused, they tax the body and stall progress.

Seasonal Training

Unless you play more than one sport, you will get the best results by training throughout the year. The reason is that muscular strength, when repeatedly worked on and maintained over time, actually becomes fixed in the muscles. To maximize this condition, coaches divide athletic training into cycles—off-season, preseason, in-season, and sometimes a postseason cycle.

The goal of each season varies according to the sport. Generally off-season training is devoted to increasing strength and power, with a program that emphasizes progressive resistance training.

Preseason training concentrates on cardiovascular fitness, muscular endurance, and explosive power. A coach may employ *circuit training*, in which athletes train with a series of exercises that work all major muscle groups, taking very little rest between exercises. Circuit training builds aerobic fitness and muscular strength at the same time.

Serge Nubret of France.

In-season training preserves the fitness levels achieved in the earlier cycles. A coach may use circuit training or a special weight training routine designed to build an athlete's weaker muscle groups.

Postseason training rehabilitates any injuries that occurred during the playing season.

Strength Means Performance

No two strength routines are ever alike. They vary from sport to sport, from athlete to athlete, and from season to season. A shot putter does not train the same way a basketball player trains. A baseball player's routine is different from a football player's. Even on a football team, a defensive lineman works out differently than a quarterback does. But despite the many differences, one universal denominator remains: Weight training builds a better athlete.

Power Clean

As a core exercise in sports, the power clean works several muscle groups at once: the frontal thighs, hips, hamstrings, lower back, abs, shoulders, traps, and biceps. In the clean, you lift a barbell from the floor to your chest in one continuous movement.

Begin in a partially squatted position and take an overgrip on the bar, with your hands spaced shoulder-width apart. Position your feet a comfortable distance apart, with toes pointing slightly outward. Keep your head up and focused on a point in front of you. Your knees should be inside your arms.

To start the clean, lift the bar from the floor using the sheer strength of your legs and hips. As you pull up, keep your arms and back straight.

When the bar is about four to five inches above your knees, begin to pull it up toward your chin, in a move similar to an upright row. Both arms and knees are flexed. Keep your elbows out and the bar close to your body. Now drop quickly under the bar, thrusting your elbows forward so that the bar can rest high on your chest and shoulders. Complete the clean by standing perfectly erect with the bar fixed upon your chest.

Chapter 13

The Nutritional Edge

Greg "Rocky" DeFerro.

Diet . . . to most people, it's just another nasty four-letter word synonymous with deprivation. If you bristle when you hear it, relax. As a bodybuilder, you eat well.

Your muscles need food so that they can grow. Skipping meals, eating too much junk food, crash dieting—these all defeat the purpose of bodybuilding. And that's to reshape the body into more attractive, healthier dimensions. The bodybuilding diet puts muscle on and takes fat off, without deprivation. It fuels your body with the right balance of protein, carbohydrates, fats, vitamins, minerals, and other health-giving nutrients. Here's what you need to know about the all-important subject of bodybuilding nutrition.

Protein

Protein builds body tissues, including muscles. It comes from meat, fish, chicken, dairy foods, vegetables, and grains. During digestion, proteins are broken down into smaller units called amino acids, which are then absorbed by the body for tissue-building.

You need twenty-two amino acids for good health. Nine of these aminos have been labeled *essential* because your body can't make them. You have to get them from food.

Because it furnishes amino acids, protein has long been linked with muscle building. For decades, athletes believed that the more steak, eggs, and milk they devoured the more muscle they would gain. But there's no proof that eating massive quantities of protein will stimulate muscle growth. In fact, protein not used by the body is packed away as fat.

The amount of protein you need each day depends on your age. In *Jane Brody's Nutrition Book* (Bantam Books), author Jane Brody gives the following formula for figuring your own requirements, based on recommended daily allowances set by the National Academy of Sciences: multiply your weight by .36, if you're nineteen or older; by .39 if you're fourteen to eighteen; and by .45 if you're eleven to fourteen. As an example, an adult who weighs 170 pounds would need about sixty-one grams a day.

It isn't hard to meet protein requirements, either. Two cups of milk, a poached egg on wheat toast, and a four-ounce cheeseburger on a bun total fifty-six grams of protein. For a well-balanced diet, about 20 to 25 percent of your daily calories should come from protein.

Bodybuilding hikes your protein needs up a bit. As trained muscles become more efficient, their protein content expands. You then need more protein, about six or seven extra grams a day—about as much as you would get from one ounce of hard cheese.

Rolf Mueller and Lee Haney.

Amino Acid Supplements—Do They Work?

Amino acid supplements are a hot item in bodybuilding. But do they build muscle? The jury is still out, though some bodybuilders claim positive results from them.

According to an article in *Prevention*, a group of bodybuilders in California has been experimenting with the aminos valine, isoleucine, and leucine—the so-called branch-chained amino acids that regulate the body's protein-building machinery—to see if the growth-producing effects of steroid drugs can be duplicated. (Steroids are synthetic male hormones that make muscle grow.) Theoretically it's possible, the article pointed out, but the secret may lie in finding the right ratio of the three amino acids. Research on the muscle-building potential of aminos still has a long way to go.

In the absence of solid information on amino acid supplements, be cautious if you decide to take them. Nutritionists warn that megadosing with aminos can endanger health, causing nutritional imbalances and possible kidney problems. It's best to get your protein from natural sources.

Carbohydrates

Carbohydrates, or *carbs*, have dethroned protein as the nutrient of athletic popularity. Most bodybuilders and athletes now swear by high-carb diets and do so for good reason. Carbohydrates (breads, grains, fruits, vegetables, and sweets) energize the body for more intense workouts.

During digestion, carbohydrates are broken down into glucose (blood sugar) to be used as energy for the red blood cells and the central nervous system. Glucose not used right away is stored in the liver and muscles as glycogen, the fuel your body runs on during workouts.

Unless you eat plenty of carbs on a daily basis, you're setting yourself up for fatigue. You'll tire easily. Your endurance will drop. Your legs will feel heavy. You'll be moody. A sluggish workout often means low levels of glycogen in the muscles. To keep those levels constant, structure your diet so that 50 to 60 percent of your daily calories comes from carbs—about four or more servings.

The kind of carbs you eat makes a difference too. Carbohydrates are *complex* (pasta, whole grains, fruits, and vegetables) or *simple* (sugars and sweets). Simple carbs reach your bloodstream almost instantly, causing a sharp rise in glucose. As a result, your pancreas releases a surge of insulin, a hormone that takes glucose from the blood and delivers it to the cells. Your blood sugar plummets and you feel weak and shaky. Complex carbs, on the other hand, are turned into glucose more slowly, giving you steady, continuing energy. Complex carbs also contain more nutrients than simple carbs.

Fat

Mr. Universe Jeff King was once so fanatical about dietary fat that he would stab holes in chicken breasts while they were being boiled so that all the fat would drain out of them. At the time, he was on a zero-fat diet.

"My body was so striated that I would have done anything to keep the definition I had," King says. "But the side effects of zero-fat dieting were alarming. My skin became extremely dry and my hair started to fall out."

King learned the hard way that you do need fats in your diet for good health. Dietary fat comes from vegetable oils, margarine, nuts and seeds, nut butters, meat, fish, poultry, and dairy products. Fat is a carrier for vitamins A, D, E, and K—the fat-soluble type, which means they need fat to be absorbed. Fat supplies essential fatty acids—nutrients from the breakdown of fat during digestion—that your body can't make on its own. Along with other nutrients, essential fatty acids keep body tissues healthy. All cells, except red blood cells and central nervous system cells, use fatty acids for energy.

Certain fats are healthier than others. Polyunsaturated fats, found in corn, soy, sunflower, and safflower oils, help prevent heart attacks and strokes because they reduce the levels of LDL cholesterol (the dangerous kind) in your blood. New studies are showing that another kind of fat, called *monosaturated*, lowers LDL cholesterol too. Monosaturated fats are found in olive, peanut, avocado, and almond oils. Avoid *saturated fats*—animal fats and coconut oil. They can clog arteries and cause high blood pressure.

Jeff King.

A fat that has been called a "nutritional breakthrough" by *Prevention* is omega-3, an unsaturated fat found in fish. So far, research indicates that omega-3 may have a role in preventing heart disease, relieving arthritic pain, and battling breast cancer.

Be moderate with fats. Too much will show up on your physique as body fat. No more than 30 percent of your total caloric intake each day should come from fat.

Vitamins and Minerals

Vitamins and minerals are vital nutrients that act as catalysts in hundreds of physiological reactions, from metabolism to growth. Numbering about twenty, vitamins are furnished by food in various amounts and are absolutely critical for good health. When you do not get enough of a certain vitamin, certain deficiency symptoms appear but can be corrected by supplementation under a doctor's care.

Vitamins are categorized as either fat-soluble (they need fat to be absorbed) or water-soluble (they dissolve in water and do not need fat for absorption). All vitamins except A, D, E, and K are water-soluble.

Vitamin needs vary according to age, sex, overall health, and level of physical activity. The best way to ensure that your vitamin requirements are being met is to eat a variety of foods.

Minerals make up bones, teeth, blood, nerve cells, and body tissues. They strengthen bones, maintain the health of the heart and brain, and keep muscles and nerves in top shape. Approximately seventeen minerals are needed for the body to function properly. Calcium, phosphorus, magnesium, potassium, sulfur, sodium, and chloride are *macronutrients* because they are needed in large amounts (but not megadoses) by the body. Other minerals, called *microminerals* or *trace minerals*, are required in smaller amounts but are still necessary for good health. All minerals essential to health must be furnished by the diet. As with vitamins, a deficiency in any one mineral can cause illness but is treatable by adding the missing mineral to the diet.

Vitamin and Mineral Supplements

Athletes and fitness buffs pop vitamins and minerals by the handful. Are supplements really necessary? In many cases they are, especially if you're dieting or not eating balanced meals. People who are heavy smokers or drinkers are often deficient in vitamins and minerals. Elderly people are candidates for supplement therapy. Women often need extra iron and calcium for deficiencies peculiar to females. With exercise, the need for certain vitamins and minerals increases, particularly vitamin C, many of the B vitamins, and the minerals iron, potassium, magnesium, and zinc. If, for some reason, you think you need supplements, check with your doctor, who can determine your need and then prescribe the right vitamin or mineral, should it be appropriate.

The average healthy person does not need to self-dose with vitamin and mineral preparations. Taking large doses of certain supplements may hurt you rather than help you. Excessive amounts of the fat-soluble vitamins are toxic. Too much vitamin A or D can retard growth and permanently damage body organs.

"People think water-soluble vitamins are safe too, even in large doses, because the excess is simply secreted in the urine," says Mary Engelland, a registered dietitian and YMCA fitness director. "But we are finding that this is not true. Excessive amounts of water-solubles can be harmful. Vitamin B_6 is a good example. High dosages cause nervous system disorders, from numbness in hands and feet to muscle incoordination."

To be on the safe side, many nutritionists recommend taking a multivitamin tablet each day—one that supplies a good balance of nutrients at recommended levels.

Sodium Alert

Sodium, a mineral found in salt, is an essential nutrient. In tandem with another mineral, potassium, sodium regulates water balance in the body. About a teaspoon a day of salt supplies the sodium you need for good health.

The problem is that salt is hidden in many of the foods we eat, especially baked goods and canned, processed, and fast foods. Therefore, it's hard to gauge how much salt we really eat in a day. Excessive sodium has been linked to high blood pressure and its life-threatening consequences, heart and kidney disease and stroke. Watching how often you tip the salt shaker is the best way to monitor your sodium intake.

Dieters should beware too. Extra salt can register a weight gain on the scales—for two reasons. First, too much salt causes water retention, which in turn means water weight gain. And second, new research has suggested that extra salt, taken with a meal that includes carbohydrate foods, actually causes the body to absorb more calories than normal.

Water

Your body's most important nutrient is water. Vital for every body process, water carries vitamins, minerals, and other nutrients throughout your body. It maintains body temperature, flushes waste out of the body, and lubricates the joints and the areas between organs.

Sixty percent of your total weight is water. Some people are afraid to drink water for fear they'll inflate with extra water weight. But depriving yourself of this vital fluid prompts water retention. Your body pulls water from cells and hoards it, and the result is bloat. To keep your body regulated, drink six to eight glasses of water a day.

Fiber

Another necessary nutrient is dietary fiber. Fiber is the indigestible portion of the foods we eat—the apple peel, the husk of grains, the outer shell of legumes. Many serious health disorders can be prevented by diets high in fiber. For instance, fiber helps prevent certain digestive tract diseases, particularly constipation, hemorrhoids, diverticulosis, and colon cancer.

Fiber is a weight loss aid too. High-fiber foods are filling and satisfy the appetite. They also speed the transit time of food in the digestive system, which means fewer calories are absorbed.

Opposite:
Cathey Palyo and
Harry Dodich.

Eat Your Way to Muscle

When Dave Hawk won the Mr. U.S.A. in 1985, he weighed 192 pounds. Competing in his first pro show six months later, he weighed 214, with 22 new pounds of rock-hard muscle. "That muscle gain," says Hawk, "was strictly from watching my diet."

A pound of muscle holds about 2,500 calories of energy. So theoretically, you need about 2,500 calories over the amount required to maintain your body weight to support one pound of muscular weight gain.

The number of calories it takes to maintain your present weight depends on your basal metabolic rate (BMR)—the number of calories your body needs to carry out normal functions such as breathing—and on the number of calories you use for physical activities each day. A rough way to figure your BMR is to multiply your present weight by ten. So if you weigh 160, your BMR calorie needs are 1,600. Then calculate your daily exercise calories. (The chart below gives estimates for the calories burned in various exercises.) Let's say you use up about 500 calories a day. Add that to 1,600 and you get 2,100—the number of calories you need each day to maintain your weight of 160.

Corinna Everson: perfection from every angle.

If you eat an extra 350 calories each day—over what your body needs to maintain its weight—you can potentially gain one pound of muscle a week while weight training. The rate at which muscular weight can be gained varies greatly from person to person. It depends on many factors, including your metabolism and body type.

On a muscle-gaining diet, your extra calories should come from nutrient-rich foods—foods high in calories and packed with vitamins and minerals. Good examples are nuts and seeds, peanut butter, dried fruits, granola, potatoes and yams, pasta, milkshakes, and cheese.

Because bodybuilding stimulates muscular weight gain, you must train consistently while trying to gain weight. If you stop exercising but keep eating, all those extra calories are likely to reappear as fat.

Calories Burned in Various Exercises (per hour)*

Aerobic Dancing	340–500
Bicycling—Moderate	240
Bicycling—Fast	415–660
Bodybuilding	300–500
Calisthenics	160
Cross-Country Skiing	700
Jogging	740–920
Jumping Rope	750
Running	900
Skiing	540
Swimming	275–500
Walking—Slow	170–240
Walking—Moderate	320
Walking—Fast	440

*Compiled from various sources.

Losing Weight

If you are "typical," says the Obesity Foundation, you go on a diet ten times a year. And, if you are successful at losing weight, you're likely to be among the 95 percent whose lost pounds will boomerang back within two years.

The best way to get off the rollercoaster of on-again, off-again dieting is to combine exercise with a prudent plan of healthy eating. To lose weight, cut back on the calories you eat and increase the number of calories you burn.

For every pound of fat you want to lose, you must cut 3,500 calories out of your diet. If you cut 500 calories and burn 500 extra calories each day, you can drop about two pounds a week—a safe rate of weight loss.

Fat Off Forever

Cutting calories is only part of the picture. Exercise is far more important—for one simple reason. A diet without exercise can make you fat. Dieting slows your metabolism. As your body adapts to fewer calories, it becomes less efficient at burning food, leading to as much as a 15 to 30 percent drop in your basal metabolic rate. If you once burned eighty calories an hour, you're now burning around fifty-five. Once off the diet, you typically eat more calories, which your body can't burn fast enough, and the pounds are back in the form of fat.

According the *setpoint theory* of weight loss, another reason diets fail is that our bodies may be genetically programmed to stay at a certain weight. Body weight is regulated by a control center in the brain. When your weight drops below its *setpoint*, this control center turns your appetite on and slows your metabolism until you put the fat back on. The setpoint theory may explain why many people diet without ever losing weight. To lower your setpoint and keep your weight under control, you must exercise.

Sergio Oliva—when not bodybuilding he is a Chicago cop!

Aerobic exercise and bodybuilding boost your fat-burning potential. In addition to using up hundreds of calories, regular aerobic exercise revs up your metabolic rate and keeps it going for at least twenty-four hours after the exercise. Aerobic exercise also activates fat-burning enzymes.

Bodybuilding stimulates your metabolism too, by increasing muscle tissue, which is metabolically more active than untoned muscle. So, day after day, your body burns calories at a fast rate even at rest.

One final point about weight loss: Do it slowly or you are apt to lose muscle. "You work so hard at gaining muscle," says professional bodybuilder Dona Oliveira. "Why sacrifice it all for a fad diet that won't work anyway?"

The Diet You Need

As a bodybuilder, you need nutrient-rich foods to train hard and build a good-looking physique. The following chart gives you your recommended number of servings each day. Choose a variety of foods from each group. If you need to lose weight, adjust your calorie intake and increase your exercise.

Nutrient Groups	Recommended Daily Servings
Dairy Products (milk, yogurt, cheese, eggs)	Teenagers: 4 or More Adults: 2 or More
Meats (lean, red meats, fish, poultry)	2 or More
Fruit and Vegetables (fresh, frozen, dried fruits and vegetables, juices, legumes, nuts, seeds)	4 or More
Grains (breads, cereals, pasta, muffins, rolls)	4 or More
Fats (vegetable and nut oils, low-calorie salad dressings)	No More than 30 Percent of Daily Calories

Chapter 14

Drugs: Deadweight in the Gym

Matt Mendenhall, Mr. U.S.A.

"Weights saved my life more than once," said popular television actor Robert Blake in the January 1986 *Muscle and Fitness*. Up until several years ago, Blake had been hooked on alcohol and prescription drugs. Today he's drug-free and says bodybuilding helped him stay that way.

Like Blake, many people are discovering that bodybuilding can be a refuge from bad habits. But the lure of body beautiful or sports superstardom can be so great that many people, from dieters to budding athletes, often seek shortcuts in their quest to look good or to be the best. Their search for the quick fix can lead to drugs.

Dr. Bob Goldman, author of the informative book *Death in the Locker Room* (Icarus Press), once asked 198 world-class athletes if they would take a magic drug with the capability of guaranteeing their victory in every competition for the next five years, knowing that the drug had one side effect—it would kill them five years after taking it. According to Goldman, 52 percent (103 athletes) said "yes," that they would die to win.

In sports and fitness, people take drugs for various reasons—to treat injuries, to lose weight, to bolster self-esteem, to gain muscle size and strength, or to improve overall physical performance. Some reasons are legitimate, others are totally counter to the ethics of fair sports and good health. Here's an overview of the drugs and other substances most prevalent in the fitness world, along with their pros and cons.

Anabolic Steroids

Anabolic steroids are synthetic male hormones that are injected or taken orally. Dr. William N. Taylor, author of *Hormonal Manipulation: A New Era of Monstrous Athletes* (McFarland and Co.), wrote in *Psychology Today*, "More than a million American athletes and fitness buffs are using anabolic steroids . . . to make themselves stronger and faster." Dr. Taylor calls his estimate "conservative."

Steroids are used widely in sports such as shot put, discus, and weightlifting, where great muscular strength is essential for performance. Athletes like bodybuilders and football players sometimes use anabolic steroids when trying to gain weight and muscle mass. Even runners and marathoners use these drugs. Sports organizations the world over condemn their use.

Steroids produce greater strength and increased muscle mass, elevate concentrations of iron in the blood, reduce body fat, and speed recovery from muscle and tendon injuries.

But steroids are dangerous. In Phoenix, a survey was conducted among twenty-four male weight-trained athletes asking them about their steroid use. Part of the survey asked about side effects experienced while on the drugs.

John Hnatyschak
and
Graeme Lancefield
of Australia.

Twenty side effects were reported, including dizziness, nausea, headache, water retention, decreased sex drive, high blood pressure, acne, testicular atrophy, hair loss, and change in mental attitude. The most common side effects were water retention, acne, and decreased sex drive. One athlete who reported kidney infection and liver damage was under a physician's care.

Serious, life-threatening cardiovascular problems have long been associated with steroids. At age thirty-three, Glenn Maur, a competitive powerlifter and bodybuilder from California, had a heart attack, brought on by continual use of steroids, and underwent an operation that required five bypasses. Of his steroid use, Maur wrote in the July 1985 issue of *Muscle and Fitness*: "Doctors say that there's a good chance my life has been considerably shortened by the flagrant way I have abused my body."

Athletes who use steroids may also risk getting AIDS (acquired immune deficiency syndrome) by sharing needles used to inject the drug, according to a report in the *NSCA Journal*. Doctors at a Mineola, New York, hospital made this conclusion after examining a thirty-seven-year-old bodybuilder they believe caught the disease in this manner.

Women who take steroids experience masculinizing effects, including increased facial hair, deepening of the voice, and enlarged clitoris, all side effects that are largely irreversible. In teenagers, steroids stop bone growth and permanently stunt growth.

Based on a thorough analysis of the scientific literature on the effects of these drugs, the National Strength and Conditioning Association has said, as part of its position statement on the use of anabolic steroids, that steroid use "poses a threat, the extent of which over the long term remains undefined, to the liver, cardiovascular, immunological and endocrine systems, and thus to overall health and longevity."

Human Growth Hormone (HGH)

Dr. Goldman calls HGH the " 'in' drug of the near future." A natural hormone extracted from the pituitary gland of cadavers, HGH is used therapeutically to treat certain types of dwarfism in children. Various forms of HGH are now being synthesized by companies in the United States and Europe. Athletes in sports in which height and size are valued are using HGH for its growth-inducing effects.

"We know that human growth hormone has a tissue-building effect on the human body, perhaps greater than any other hormones," wrote Dr. Taylor in *The Futurist*.

The potential side effects of HGH administered to healthy individuals are frightening. According to Dr. Goldman in *Death in the Locker Room*, problems associated with HGH include hepatitis, hypoglycemia, and diabetes, with the likelihood of coma in susceptible people, and acromegaly, a disorder in which the feet, hands, fingers, nose, jaw, and soft tissues of the face grow, causing the face to take on a "Frankenstein" look.

Amphetamines

Better known as speed or uppers, amphetamines are central nervous system stimulants that are highly habit forming. Tolerance builds up quickly, forcing users to increase their doses. While on these drugs, a person feels extremely confident, alert, and energized—all reasons why athletes like to take them to get ready for a game. Amphetamines have also been prescribed for weight loss because they decrease the appetite.

These drugs have allowed cyclists and other endurance athletes to push beyond their bodies' physical limits—a state that puts them at risk of circulatory collapse. In the sixties, several world-class athletes died as a result of amphetamine use.

The side effects of amphetamines are well-known and include stomach and intestinal problems, rapid heart rate, and insomnia. Very high doses can cause hallucinations and panic attacks.

Diuretics

Diuretics are sometimes used by bodybuilders just before competition to achieve an ultra-defined look. By increasing the rate of urine formation, these drugs remove fluids from the body.

Diuretic use is a dangerous habit for bodybuilders to adopt. Along with the fluids are flushed potassium, calcium, phosphorus, and magnesium—all essential minerals for the body. The resulting look is not one of sharply defined cuts, but more of a stringy, tired appearance.

Loss of these critical nutrients poses considerable health risks, especially if the use of diuretics is long-term. One international bodybuilding competitor died from excessive use of diuretics.

Diuretics do have a valid therapeutic use and are commonly prescribed for people with heart and kidney disorders.

Rick Valente.

Recreational Drugs

Abuse of the recreational drugs alcohol, marijuana, and cocaine continues to be a serious problem, even among fitness buffs, athletes and nonathletes alike. Anyone whose goal is to build a better body should realize that in the long run recreational drugs destroy both physical and mental health.

The most widely used of all drugs is alcohol, a potentially addictive substance. Too much of it interferes with the absorption of vitamins and minerals in the small intestine. If you're dieting, watch your consumption of alcohol, for not only is it high in calories and in sugar, it also hinders fat metabolism. Alcohol is dehydrating too and leads to water retention. It has a detrimental effect on all athletic performance.

There is nothing wrong with moderate use of alcohol (no more than two drinks a day). In fact, medical researchers have discovered that alcohol encourages the formation of HDL cholesterol, which is thought to help reduce the chance of heart disease by preventing the "bad" LDL cholesterol from accumulating on artery walls. Exercise, however, has the same effect.

Better known as pot, weed, or grass, marijuana is a drug made from the dried leaves of the Cannabis sativa plant. When smoked it gives a sense of euphoria, often accompanied by mood changes and impaired motor skills. Athletes have used it to relax before competition. Long-term use of marijuana irritates the respiratory tract.

The addictive properties of marijuana are often downplayed. Says one professional athlete, now recovered from an addiction to marijuana after participating in Narcotics Anonymous (NA): "I had a hard time with pot. It was my drug of choice. People would tell me, 'Pot is no big deal. Everyone smokes it.' But I could not get clean. I could not stop smoking pot. I'd buy a bag, smoke a joint, and then hate the way I felt. I'd flush it down the toilet, and as soon as I'd straighten up, I'd go buy some more. It was insanity."

The drug cocaine is a white crystalline powder made from the leaves of the coca plant. Cocaine has become linked with big-time collegiate and pro athletics, especially since the deaths of University of Maryland basketball star Len Bias and Cleveland Browns' Don Rogers were blamed on its use.

Cocaine is highly addictive. When injected or taken through the nose, it stimulates the central nervous system, producing a range of effects, including euphoria, restlessness, and tremors. Among the most serious effects of cocaine are damage to the cardiovascular system and to fetuses.

Caffeine

On the safer end of the scale is caffeine, a legal drug found in coffee, tea, soft drinks, chocolate, and some over-the-counter medications.

Tom Platz.

Caffeine has long been touted as a sports aid, especially by endurance athletes who want to run, cycle, or swim longer in races. Apparently, caffeine improves endurance by mobilizing fatty acids for energy early in the race and saving glycogen stores until later on. This sparing of muscle fuel helps athletes avoid "hitting the wall"—a painful phenomenon that occurs when muscles run out of glycogen during endurance competition.

Caffeine has also been found to increase metabolic rate—one reason why bodybuilders use it to help them lose body fat. Taken before workouts, caffeine also postpones muscular fatigue.

Be prudent in your use of caffeine, however. It has been linked to heart trouble. Overuse of caffeine (*caffeinism*) causes anxiety, restlessness, diarrhea, headaches, and heart palpitations.

It's Your Body

Superhuman strength, a glorious sports career, a body full of bigger-than-life muscles—these are all dreams that can make drugs a powerful temptation. Is it worth the risk?

"Taking them is an individual choice," says Dr. Goldman. "But you can hurt yourself by messing around with dangerous drugs. If you play, you're going to pay."

Dave Hawk,
U.S.A.

Chapter 15

On Stage

Mike Christian.

Once you've been bodybuilding awhile, your friends might encourage you to compete, especially if you've gained a respectable amount of muscle size. But bodybuilding competition? Doesn't that mean flexing your biceps and triceps on stage before hundreds, maybe even thousands, of people . . . donning a bathing suit half the size of the one you wear to the beach . . . slicking your skin with shiny oil? Naturally, you're hesitant. Is bodybuilding competition really for you?

"I had been training for four months when my husband (then my boyfriend) told me I should enter a bodybuilding contest. My immediate reaction was 'Not me! I'm not going to compete!'" recalls Marjo Selin, today one of pro bodybuilding's top women competitors.

"I was very shy and had always avoided anything that had to do with performing. Speeches for school gave me the shakes for weeks. But eventually the idea of competing sounded attractive. I entered and placed second. I was surprised by how much I liked the contest. Afterward, I began to enjoy the idea of training hard, of having a goal, of working toward that goal. I began to achieve more in every way."

You'd be surprised at how many of today's top bodybuilders were once reluctant about competition but took friends' advice to compete, and over time and with successive contests metamorphosized into extroverted superstars. Of course, not everyone who competes is destined for Olympian glory. But bodybuilding, besides being a superb conditioning system, also happens to be a sport. That fact alone is often enough to stir even the most dormant competitive drive.

Don't worry about feeling nervous. As Lou Ferrigno advised in *Muscle Mag International*, "It's only natural. Entering contests should be seen as a tool to give you a goal to work toward and as an incentive for getting into your best possible shape."

The First Step

Champion bodybuilders agree that before you compete for the first time, you must go to a bodybuilding contest as a spectator and learn what competition is all about. Be a keen observer. Study the contest's format—how it is organized and what the competitors are required to do. Watch the competitors carefully, making mental notes about what you liked and did not like about their performances. Sitting in the audience of a bodybuilding competition is excellent preparation for your own debut on the posing platform.

Amateur contests are sanctioned by one of two national organizations, the Amateur Athletic Union (AAU) or the National Physique Committee (NPC), which is affiliated with the International Federation of Bodybuilders (IFBB).

By law, you can compete in contests of both the AAU and the NPC, without fear of being penalized by either organization.

In the beginning, concentrate on getting as much contest experience as possible. As champion bodybuilder Cathey Palyo said in the June 1986 issue of *Strength Training for Beauty*, "When you start out, it's good to compete a lot because you have a better chance of winning and that will get your confidence up."

The Precontest Diet

In competition, one criterion you'll be judged on is *definition*—the visual detail of your muscles—a quality achieved primarily through precontest dieting. A healthy precontest diet rids your body of extra fat without sacrificing muscle size and gives you that prized look bodybuilders call *ripped*.

Start your precontest diet as early as eight to twelve weeks before a show, to lose body fat gradually, at the rate of no more than one or two pounds a week. If you drop weight any faster than that, you'll be shedding precious muscle tissue, resulting in a physique that looks shriveled and a body that feels weak.

By dieting intelligently, you can eat a variety of healthy foods and still lose fat. For precontest diets, bodybuilders typically choose these foods, formulated into daily menus at caloric levels that will promote fat loss:

DAIRY PRODUCTS. Skim milk, low-fat plain yogurt, cottage cheese, eggs and egg whites, cholesterol-free egg products.

MEAT, CHICKEN, AND FISH. Lean red meats, chicken (white meat), turkey (white meat), tuna fish (water-packed), white fish such as flounder, sole, cod, or perch (dry-broiled).

FRUITS AND VEGETABLES. Bananas, pineapples, apples, oranges, grapefruits, melons, strawberries, and other fresh fruits, salads made with green, leafy vegetables prepared without dressing, fresh vegetables such as broccoli, cauliflower, or zucchini steamed and served plain, baked potato, baked sweet potato, or yams.

BREADS AND GRAINS. Whole wheat bread, oatmeal, cream of wheat, bran muffins, brown rice, rice cakes, whole wheat pasta.

Training and Aerobics

Up to now, your training has been designed to build extra muscle mass. With the contest near, it's time to work on muscular shape and definition. You do that by changing your workout to include fewer compound exercises and more isolation exercises, performed with lighter weights and more repetitions, with less rest between sets. If your schedule permits, work out on a split routine to increase your number of training days.

Include extra aerobics in your precontest training too. Aerobic activity burns fat for better definition. All bodybuilders have their favorite aerobic exercises. Tom Platz rides a bicycle. Tina Plakinger jumps rope. Lynn Conkright runs up and down bleachers. Marjo Selin walks. The key is to find an aerobic activity you enjoy and do it several times a week, but for no more than forty-five minutes each time. Muscle mass drops when you overdo aerobics.

The Art of Posing

If you could go back in time to the forties to attend a physique show, you'd be entertained by a hand-balancing act, a few comedy routines, dumbbell juggling, and a beauty contest—all staged before the main event, the actual bodybuilding competition.

Bodybuilding competition has come a long way since then. Today, there's no need for extra glitz and glitter at physique shows, and for one simple reason: posing. Today's competitors have taken the art of posing to new levels of drama and excitement. Posing is all the entertainment a show needs. It is the show.

As a beginning competitor, you'll have the edge on your opponents if you can master posing. The most accomplished posers in bodybuilding shows often place much higher than the most muscular competitors. At all levels, contests have been won and lost on posing alone.

In competition, judges evaluate your physique by watching you go through a series of *compulsory* poses, flexed positions you are required to know. There are seven of these: front double biceps, front lat spread, side chest, back double biceps, rear lat spread, side triceps, and abdominal and thigh pose. In men's contests, judges sometimes ask to see a pose called the *most muscular*, also called the *crab* because the arms are clenched together in front of the body like a crab's claws. The competitor then flexes his entire body, and if he's in good shape, his traps, delts, chest, and arms burst into well-defined cords of strapping muscle. At that point, the audience goes wild. The most muscular is a real crowd pleaser.

To learn the compulsory poses, study photographs of competitors in bodybuilding magazines, seek out knowledgeable people at your gym who have competed and who are willing to coach you on posing, and then practice in front of a mirror every chance you get.

A few months before your contest, begin choreographing your posing routine—a free-style presentation performed to music. Your routine lets you present your physique from its best, most advantageous angles.

Canada's John Cardillo works hard at the alternate dumbbell curl.

"If you are a relative beginner or are unsure about how to select the poses that suit you, compare yourself to some top physique champion," says Mike Mentzer, writing in *Muscle Mag International*. "If your physique 'tends' to resemble [Frank] Zane's, you might carefully study his poses in the various muscle magazines and try to adapt them to your physique."

When mapping out a posing routine, NPC Collegiate National Champion Todd King says to incorporate all the compulsory poses. "I start with a front lat spread, go into the double biceps, and turn left for a side chest pose. I continue rotating left, always moving in the same direction, for my back shots, the lat spread and double biceps, following up with another side pose. I then go into a lunge and finish up with the most muscular. I use about ten to twelve poses. It's basic but it wins."

When you do perform your routine, hold your poses long enough for the judges to properly evaluate your muscularity. Make smooth and graceful transitions from pose to pose. Develop *signature poses* too—unique poses that highlight your muscles from the best angles.

Music is critical to a good routine. Should you choose instrumentals or

Kevin Lawrence and Diana Dennis are among the greatest entertainers in bodybuilding.

vocals? A tempo that's fast or slow? A Top Forty song or a golden oldie? If you ask around, you're apt to get conflicting advice on this one. Music is very personal.

"Choose music that is current and upbeat," advises Kay Baxter, an accomplished poser. "But don't pick something that is too fast, unless you're a good dancer and can choreograph snappy moves that fit the routine. One of the best ways to find good music for bodybuilding is to go to an aerobic dance class, listen to the music, and watch how the students move to it. Dance instructors can give you good ideas for music too. They know the best music for body movement."

Carla Dunlap, one of the most creative posers in bodybuilding today, offered this advice in the June 1986 issue of *Muscular Development* on moving to music: "Your moves and poses shouldn't just happen along with the music; they should highlight and interpret the music. Here you have a choice. Your moves can pick up different parts of the music: pulse or basic tempo, melody, rhythm, lyrics (if your music has any), and accent and climaxes. Use these for excitement points."

Practice your routine and your compulsories over and over again until they become rote. Visualize yourself performing perfectly on stage. Each time you practice, have a friend videotape your performance. Then critique yourself on tape to sharpen your performance to its finest degree.

Don't Bloat

Near showtime, some bodybuilders have to contend with water retention, a condition that can swiftly inflate an otherwise perfectly chiseled physique. It's frustrating to look as if you've gained five pounds when in reality you've been cutting up for weeks. Today, competitors have learned healthy ways to solve this problem, without resorting to health-robbing diuretics.

Being bloated means that you have too much water under the skin. That water should be inside the cells. To keep water in the cells, competitors cut their sodium intake and increase their potassium levels by taking potassium supplements a few days before the show. The potassium helps drive water back into the cells to give the muscles a more defined, fuller appearance.

Be sure to drink plenty of water while preparing for a contest. If you restrict water intake, your body will extract water from your muscle cells, resulting in bloat.

Because ordinary tap water contains sodium, chlorine, and other chemicals, drink distilled water, which is chemical-free, especially during the two weeks before a contest. Distilled water keeps your body cleansed and free from bloat.

Looking Good

In your contest preparation, there are a few cosmetic matters to take care of. The first is tanning. A good tan makes your cuts more prominent. But suntanning can be damaging to the skin. If you tan under the sun, do it slowly over time, using a sunscreen to prevent burning. With tanning booths, follow safe procedures as outlined by the tanning salon. Again, tan gradually.

Several cosmetic companies have now developed sunless tanning lotions that give your skin a golden brown color. Unlike the tan-in-a-bottle products of years ago that left your skin looking orange, these lotions, called *self-tanners*, create a natural-looking tan. The color forms when the ingredients in the lotion combine with the amino acids in your skin. Among the companies now producing self-tanners are Avon, Lancome, Biotherm, and Clarins.

Competitors also use a product called Dy-O-Derm, a cosmetic stain that darkens the skin to suntanned hues. Apply it the night before your contest, making sure that it covers your skin evenly.

Renel Janvier, Tony Melville.

In addition to tanning, the color of your bathing suit is an important part of your total look. "Choose a color that enhances your skin tone and hair coloring," advises pro Dona Oliveira. "Dark-haired competitors look best in red, white, fuchsia, or royal blue; and blondes in pink, or turquoise, or green."

Your bathing suit should fit well and complement your symmetry. Many professional competitors now have their suits made for them by qualified designers to assure a fit that accentuates the physique.

The Last Week

The week before the show, many bodybuilders practice carbohydrate loading, a dietary and training system that lasts one week and results in better definition. The object of carbohydrate loading is to first deplete your muscles of glycogen and then reload them with glycogen to make them look full and peaked. Here's how it works.

From Sunday through Wednesday, perform high-repetition training and moderate aerobics to burn up glycogen in the muscles. Follow a low-carb diet with ample protein to further deplete glycogen stores.

From Thursday through Saturday, stop all training to let glycogen rebuild in the muscles. Replace your training with intense posing sessions—which do not burn up much glycogen but give your physique a harder, more defined look. Posing also conditions you for the endurance you will need for the long hours of competition. Your muscles will look fuller by Saturday too, especially when you *pump up*—perform light bodybuilding exercises before going on stage. Pumping up inflates muscles with extra blood to make them look more massive.

In addition, switch to a high-carbohydrate diet consisting of complex carbs such as fruits, vegetables, rice, baked potatoes, and whole wheat bread. Remember to keep your sodium levels low and drink plenty of distilled water.

If you're at risk for certain diseases, including cardiovascular disease and diabetes, it may be dangerous for you to carbohydrate load. Check with your doctor before trying this regimen.

Showtime

The day has finally arrived, and if you're like most competitors, from seasoned amateurs to veteran Olympians, you'll wake up nervous. But that's good. Nervousness will keep you on your toes for the long day ahead.

One of the first tasks to attend to before you head for the contest is to pack your competition care package, including items such as:

Marjo Selin and
Juliette Bergman.

- An extra posing suit or two, just in case yours gets torn, dirty, or smudged with oil.
- Grooming items (makeup, hair spray, comb and brush, blow dryer, shaver, and so forth).
- Water bottle filled with distilled water.
- Natural snack foods—fresh fruits, raisins, rice cakes—to sustain energy levels.
- Oil (Seasoned bodybuilders recommend a light suntan oil for the best look under the lights).
- Two or three cassette copies of your recorded posing music, with your name clearly marked on the tape.
- Towels.
- Rubberized cables or surgical tubing to use for pumping up.

At the contest, all competitors are divided into classes—weight classes if it is an NPC contest and height classes if it is an AAU contest. Contests are conducted according to rounds.

In round one, the judges study the competitors in relaxed positions from four angles—both sides, front, and back. This round gives the judges a chance to evaluate your symmetry—the proportions of your overall muscular development.

During round two, you will be asked to go through your compulsory poses. The judges will rate you on muscularity, separation, and definition. The better your visual detail, the better your chances are for a high score.

In most contests, rounds one and two are scored during prejudging, a block of time before the main show. Round three, in which the competitors present their posing routines, is a part of the main show. Besides overall muscular development, the judges are grading you on poise, confidence, and overall personality on stage. Good stage presence, with appropriate facial expressions, is a plus in competition.

Mr. America,
Gary Leonard.

As the competition nears the finale, the judges announce the top places (usually five) and ask the finalists to go through a *posedown*. For about two minutes, the finalists battle it out by going through a series of poses so that the judges can have one last look before choosing the winner.

The Many Faces of Victory

The very fact of competition means that there will be winners and losers. How you handle victory and defeat says a great deal about your character.

Take Tom Platz, for example. He says he's one of the few pros to establish a career from losing rather than from winning, yet he is one of the most popular bodybuilders in the world today. If a prize were given at the Mr. Olympia for crowd favorite, Platz would win every time. Why? The reason is simple. On or off stage, Tom Platz sees himself as a winner. And it comes through. "I feel good about myself because I give the sport everything I have," he says. This attitude is the mark of a true champion.

Win or lose, the point is that you gave the competition your very best. "When you give anything your total effort," says Jeff King, "you win, regardless of the outcome. It's the personal satisfaction of knowing you did your best that makes you a winner."

Chapter 16

Pumping Up Mentally

Mike Mentzer.

Bodybuilding has the power to hook you. Of all exercise programs, bodybuilding makes the most dramatic changes in your body. You see results quickly. You feel inspired by the transformation. Bodybuilding is such an excellent physical and mental booster that you won't want to give it up. Why revert to the old you when you've worked so hard on the new model?

To get hooked, you have to stick with it. Unfortunately, more than half the people who start any fitness program drop out within six months. And many of the dropouts last no longer than two weeks.

"Most gyms and health clubs have a very high percentage of quitters. People just don't know what it takes," says Nina Schoenbaum, director of the Women's Mid-City Bodybuilding Gym in New York City.

What does it take to integrate bodybuilding into your life? Attitude, mainly. Unless you're mentally committed to getting into shape, you won't last long in the gym. Build your body by using your head. Adopt what Arnold Schwarzenegger calls *want power*—the mental determination to stay with your exercise program and get the results you want. Here are some tips to help you do just that:

IMAGINE. When Schwarzenegger was a young bodybuilder, he plastered pictures of his idol Mr. Universe Reg Park all over his bedroom walls. His goal was to build a body like Park's. By using a form of *imagery* to motivate himself, he visualized what he wanted to look like.

At first, his parents thought he was crazy; after all, most boys his age tacked up girlie pictures on their walls. But all along, Schwarzenegger had a very clear vision of where he wanted to go with his body and his career. He loved being in the gym, for every rep brought him closer to the body he wanted. Psychologists will tell you: What you believe, your body achieves.

SET GOALS. Goals are your blueprint for success. They give you the incentive to stick with your program. Write them down too. This crystallizes them in your mind. Make sure your goals are reachable. Don't write down that you want to gain an inch of muscle on your arm in one month or drop ten pounds in ten days. You'll only set yourself up for failure, which in turn jeopardizes your stick-to-it potential. Take it day by day, workout by workout.

DO IT FOR YOU. Your goals have to be your own. If you decide to get into shape for someone else, you're bound to fail. "Some people have a false interest in working out," says bodybuilder Todd King. "They go to the gym just to be close to their boyfriend, girlfriend, husband, or wife. To really succeed, you must be personally convinced that bodybuilding will be good for you. Don't do it for anyone but yourself. It must be your decision and yours alone."

GET SUPPORT. An excellent motivator is to bodybuild with a friend. Make a pact with a friend to exercise together and keep each other motivated. Another person's willpower may be just what you need when you're tempted to skip a workout.

Keep at it and you'll get another kind of support from your friends . . . compliments on your new shape. "Compliments keep you fired up. They're great incentives," says Bill Norberg, an AAU Collegiate Mr. America.

STRUCTURE YOURSELF. People too often fall back on the excuse "I'm too busy to work out." Nonsense! If you care about your body, you'll carve out enough time to exercise no matter how busy you are.

The secret is structure. Our daily lives tick away with the clock. We get up in the morning, go to work, have meals, and go to bed. The next day, the schedule starts over again. Put your workout into that framework. Train on the same days and at same times every week, with as little break in the schedule as possible. Eventually, your workouts will become as cemented in your daily routine as brushing your teeth or going to the office.

VARIETY. Instead of the same stale routine you've been doing, try new ways to work out. Experiment with split routines, new grips or handles, techniques like supersetting or pre-exhaustion. Work out with heavy weights and low reps one month, and light weights and high reps the next. And mix your routine up with new combinations of machine exercises and free weight lifts.

"Muscles get bored just like people," Nina Schoenbaum says. "Not only is it important mentally to keep changing your routine, it's also important physically so that your muscles are always stimulated. Variety helps development."

There are hundreds of bodybuilding exercises too, so learn new ones. After a while, you'll discover certain exercises you like better than others. To make your workouts fun, do the exercises you like.

SMARTEN UP. Schoenbaum encourages her gym members to continually educate themselves on bodybuilding. "Keep up with current information. It might turn you on to a new idea and give you a chance to experiment with a technique you've never tried before," she says.

Prime yourself by reading bodybuilding magazines and books and by attending contests and seminars. Write to pro bodybuilders for their training manuals and other materials. There's plenty of inspiration out there to keep you going.

GET REWARDED. "Bodybuilding demands that you push your body hard," says pro Kay Baxter. "But if you can stick it out as a bodybuilder, you will be healthy."

Your body is built for activity. List the rewards you get from keeping it active: "I'll look better." "I'll feel good." "I'll live longer." "I'll have more energy." "I'll like myself better."

Think about these rewards every day. Post them on your desk, stick them on your refrigerator or bathroom mirror—any place you're apt to see them.

FIND STRENGTH. There are times when life seems to be falling down around us, times when we feel weak emotionally. A strong, healthy body gives you the confidence and self-assurance to take on any new challenge, no matter how difficult it may seem. Find comfort in knowing that you have the physical strength to carry you through any situation.

Thoughts and feelings are hard to control. If you can first get control over your body, you can begin to get control over other parts of your life. Start with the physical and the emotional will follow.

Arnold and Franco watch Jusup Wilcosz perform supine flyes.

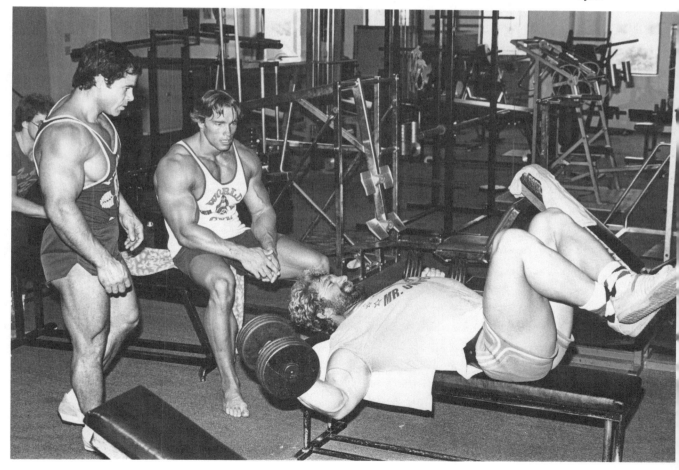

Gladys Portugues.

True Commitment

If you ever get tempted to throw in your gym towel, here's a story about true commitment to bodybuilding, about how a person would go to any lengths to keep up personal health and fitness.

During World War II, an Air Force sergeant named Richard Derby was shot down by the Germans and held for nineteen months in Austria at a prisoner-of-war camp. There, Derby and his fellow prisoners constructed one 225-pound adjustable barbell by cutting over 4,000 tin cans into flat pieces of metal, weaving these pieces together into discs, and pressing the discs into metal cases. The cases became plates, and a pipe became the bar.

Sharing this single homemade barbell, the prisoners worked out on an elaborate exercise routine consisting primarily of pressing exercises. One man who had joined the Army weighing 121 pounds increased his weight to 165 after a year's training with the weights while imprisoned at the camp. Not bad, considering the prisoners subsisted on cabbage soup and black bread. "Without weightlifting," Derby wrote in *IronMan*, "my health would have been much poorer at the end of the war."

Now that's commitment! From commitment, you get discipline. Most bodybuilders agree that the discipline you learn from bodybuilding crosses over into every facet of your life. Discipline gives you the power to be a success.

Lift for Life

Bodybuilding is a lifetime commitment, not a New Year's resolution or a crash course to make a bathing suit fit. If you look at it as something you will do for as long as you're able, you have the right attitude to build a fit body and to keep it that way for a long time. And that attitude gives you life's greatest fortune . . . your health.

Body Words

AAU (Amateur Athletic Union): A sports organization that handles amateur physique contests such as the Mr. and Ms. America.

Aerobic exercise: Continuous-action exercise that can be carried on within the body's ability to use and process oxygen efficiently. Examples include running, jogging, swimming, bicycling, and cross-country skiing.

Alternate grip: A combination of an underhand and an overhand grip in one exercise.

Amino acids: Basic building blocks of protein necessary for growth and metabolism.

Amphetamines: Highly addictive drugs that stimulate the central nervous system.

Anabolic steroids: Male hormone drugs that increase muscular size and strength.

Anaerobic exercise: Intense exercise characterized by brief bursts of effort. Anaerobic exercise puts the body in an oxygen debt, which means the cardiovascular system cannot meet the demands of the working muscles. Weight training and sprinting are two examples of anaerobic exercise.

Antagonists: Pairs of muscle groups that oppose each other, such as biceps and triceps or quadriceps and hamstrings.

Atrophy: The loss of muscle size.

Barbell: A long bar with adjustable or fixed plates at each end.

Basal metabolic rate (BMR): The number of calories the body needs for basic functions such as breathing.

Bench press: One of the three competitive power lifts; also a basic exercise for building the pectoral muscles of the chest.

Bodybuilding: A conditioning system to develop muscle size and shape through a combination of weight training exercises and proper nutrition. Bodybuilding is also a competitive sport, in which contestants are judged on muscularity, symmetry, and posing.

Body type: A system of classifying physiques according to overall structure, amount of muscle, and degree of body fat.

Cables: Weight training equipment with pulleys connected to adjustable weight stacks. Cables feature a selection of grips and handles.

Calisthenics: Exercises that do not use weights but are designed to improve muscle tone and endurance.

Calorie: Unit of energy from food.

Carbohydrate loading: A dietary system used by bodybuilders and endurance athletes. High-protein–low-carbohydrate dieting is first used to deplete the body's glycogen. Glycogen is then replaced in the muscles and liver by high-carbohydrate dieting.

Carbohydrates: Food compounds that serve as chief energy sources for the body. Fruit, vegetables, and grains are carbohydrate foods.

Cardiovascular fitness: The ability of the heart and blood vessels to adequately circulate blood and oxygen throughout the body.

Circuit training: A series of exercises that work all the major muscle groups with little rest between sets. Circuit training improves cardiovascular fitness and builds muscular size and strength.

Collars: Circular fittings placed on the ends of barbells and dumbbells to keep the plates from sliding off.

Compound: An exercise that works several muscle groups at once.

Compulsory poses: Flexed positions a bodybuilder is required to know for competition.

Contraction: Muscular motion.

Core lifts: Basic exercises designated by a coach for athletes in a strength training routine.

Cut: The delineation of a muscle from its surrounding body fat.

Cycling: Method of training in which routines are organized into periods of varying intensity.

Deadlift: One of the three competitive powerlifts; also a weight training exercise that builds the lower back, thighs, and hips.

Definition: Clarity of muscular detail and absence of body fat.

Descending sets: A system of sets that begins with heavy weights and decreases to light weights each consecutive set.

Diuretics: Drugs that increase the rate of urine formation in the body.

Dumbbell: Short bar with adjustable or fixed plates at both ends.

Ectomorphy: Slender body type characterized by long limbs and the absence of body fat.

Endomorphy: Body type characterized by a round, soft physique, with extra body fat.

Estrogen: Female hormone responsible for menstruation and the development of secondary sex characteristics (e.g., breasts).

Failure: The point of exhaustion in an exercise, at which the muscles are unable to complete additional reps.

Fats: Food substances that serve as energy sources for the body.

Flexibility: The ability of a muscle to move easily through its full range of motion.

Forced reps: Additional repetitions performed after reaching failure, with help from a training partner.

Form: Exercise style.

Free weights: Barbells, dumbbells, and ankle or wrist weights.

General warmup: Light, whole-body exercise that elevates muscle temperature to prepare the body for working out.

Generic equipment: Exercise benches, slant boards, and chinning bars.

Giant sets: Four or five different exercises, usually for the same body part, performed one right after the other without rest in between.

Glucose: Blood sugar.

Glycogen: Glucose stored by the liver and muscles. Glycogen is an energy source for the body during workouts.

Hormones: Chemicals in the body that control various physical processes.

Human growth hormone (HGH): Drug with a tissue-building effect used to treat dwarfism in children.

Hypertrophy: Increase in muscle fiber size.

IFBB (International Federation of Bodybuilders): An international sports organization that sponsors professional bodybuilding events, including the Mr. and Ms. Olympia.

Insertion: Point where the muscle is attached to the bone it moves.

Intensity: Degree of effort exerted during exercise.

Isolation: An exercise that works a single muscle or a part of a muscle.

Joint: The intersection of two bones.

Layoff: Time period in which a bodybuilder or other athlete does not train.

Lifting belt: Leather belt used for lower-back support during heavy training.

Ligaments: Fibrous bands of tissue that connect the bones at joints.

Limited-range lifts: A strength building technique performed on a power rack to allow lifting through a set range of motion.

Lockout: The full extension of limbs in a weight training exercise.

Mass: Muscle size.

Mesomorphy: Muscular body type.

Metabolic rate: The speed at which the body converts food to energy.

Metabolism: The conversion of food into energy by the body.

Mineral: A nutrient needed by the body for growth.

Muscles: Body tissue composed of hairlike fibers that contract and relax.

Muscular endurance: Ability of a muscle to repeat contractions over an extended period of time without fatigue.

Negative: The lowering portion of a weight training exercise.

Negative-accentuated training: The trainee lifts the weight with two limbs, then lowers it with one, emphasizing the lowering portion of the exercise.

Negative-only exercise: A partner raises the weight; the trainee then slowly lowers it.

NPC (National Physique Committee): Amateur arm of the International Federation of Bodybuilders (IFBB).

Nutrition: The use of food for growth and development.

Origin: Point on the bone where a muscle is anchored.

Overtraining: A condition resulting from doing too much work too soon, generally characterized by such symptoms as fatigue, decrease in strength, and weight loss.

Partial movements: Short, half-range movements of an exercise designed for extra stimulation of muscle fibers. Also called *burns*.

Personal trainer: A fitness instructor who works with trainees individually.

Plates: Disc-shaped weights used on barbells and dumbbells.

Posing: In bodybuilding competition, display of the physique to show one's muscularity.

Posing routine: A group of poses choreographed to music for bodybuilding competition.

Power: Ability of a muscle or group of muscles to move heavy objects quickly over distance.

Powerlifting: A competitive weight training sport in which contestants are judged on the amount of weight they can lift in the bench press, squat, and deadlift.

Power rack: Weight training equipment with supports for barbells and adjustable pins to allow lifting through a set range of motion.

Pre-exhaustion: A training system that works a muscle with an isolation exercise first, followed immediately by a compound exercise. Pre-exhaustion gives large muscle groups maximum stimulation.

Progressive resistance: A gradual increase in the intensity of weight training work, usually by lifting heavier and heavier weights.

Protein: Food compound necessary for growth and repair of body tissues. Protein is furnished by meat, fish, poultry, dairy products, vegetables, and grains.

Pump: Temporary inflation of muscle size from increased blood flow to the muscles being worked.

Pyramiding: A system of sets that begins with a light weight and high repetitions and increases to heavier poundage and lower reps in each consecutive set.

Range of motion: The full path of an exercise from beginning to end.

Recuperation: The time a muscle needs for rest and repair before being worked again, usually about one day.

Repetitions (reps): The number of times an exercise is performed.

Resistance: The weight of a barbell, dumbbell, or machine, or one's own body weight.

Rest-pause: A series of one or two reps with heavy weight, followed by a short rest period.

Ripped: Extreme muscular definition, with very little body fat.

Routine: A grouping of exercises.

Seasonal training: Athletic training that is divided into periods, each with a specific goal (for example, strength building, aerobic conditioning, strength maintenance, injury rehabilitation).

Sets: A group of repetitions.

Single: The maximum poundage that can be lifted for one repetition.

Specific warmup: Light exercises that warm up a certain muscle or muscle group (as opposed to the entire body).

Split routine: A training system in which different body parts are worked on different days. For instance, the lower body is trained on Monday and Thursday; the upper body, on Tuesday and Friday.

Spotter: A person who helps a trainee in the performance of an exercise.

Squat: One of the three powerlifts; also a basic leg training exercise to build lower-body strength and size.

Strength: The ability of a muscle or group of muscles to exert force during muscular contraction.

Strength training: Athletic weight training routines designed to improve strength and power in specific sports.

Supersets: Two different exercises, usually for the same muscle or for antagonistic muscles, performed one right after the other, without rest in between.

Supination: To turn the palms forward when performing dumbbell curls.

Symmetry: The overall shape of the body, especially the degree of balanced proportion among muscle groups.

Tendon: Fibrous bands of tissue that connect skeletal muscles to bones.

Testosterone: Male hormone responsible for the development of secondary sex characteristics (for example, deep voice and facial hair).

Tie-in: Point on the body where two different muscle groups meet.

Trisets: Three exercises for the same muscle performed one right after the other without rest in between.

Variable resistance: The change in the amount of resistance at various points during an exercise.

Vitamins: Food substances that regulate metabolism and growth.

Weightlifting: An Olympic weight training sport in which contestants are judged in two lifts—the snatch and the clean and jerk.

Weight stack machines: Weight training equipment that employs a stack of weights that can be adjusted according to the poundage an individual wants to lift.

Weight training: The use of barbells, dumbbells, and machines to build muscle and develop strength.

Bibliography

Books

Auchincloss, Eva. *Women's Sports Foundation Fitness and Sports Resource Guide.* Palo Alto: Women's Sports Publications, Inc., 1983.

Bass, Clarence. *Ripped 2.* Albuquerque, New Mexico: Clarence Bass' Ripped Enterprises, 1982.

Brody, Jane. *Jane Brody's Nutrition Book.* New York: Bantam Books, 1981.

Darden, Ellington. *How Your Muscles Work.* Winter Park, Florida: Anna Publishing, Inc., 1978.

Dobson, James C. *Preparing For Adolescence.* New York: Bantam Books, 1980.

Goldman, Bob, with Patricia Bush and Ronald Klatz. *Death in the Locker Room.* South Bend, Indiana: Icarus Press, 1984.

Gray, Henry. *Gray's Anatomy.* New York: Bounty Books, 1977.

Henig, Robin Marantz. *How a Woman Ages.* New York: Ballantine Books, 1985.

Illustrated Encyclopedia of the Human Body. New York: Exeter Books, 1984.

Kirschmann, John. *Nutrition Almanac,* rev. ed. New York: McGraw-Hill Book Co., 1979.

Mirkin, Gabe, and Marshall Hoffman. *Sports Medicine Book.* Boston: Little, Brown & Co., 1978.

O'Shea, John Patrick. *Scientific Principles and Methods of Strength Training.* Reading, Massachusetts: Addison-Wesley Publishing Co., 1969.

Pesman, Curtis. *How a Man Ages.* New York: Ballantine Books, 1984.

Pirie, Lynn, with Bill Reynolds. *Getting Built.* New York: Warner Books, 1984.

Riley, Dan (ed.). *Strength Training by the Experts.* West Point: Leisure Press, 1977.

Schwarzenegger, Arnold, with Douglas Kent Hall. *The Education of a Bodybuilder.* New York: Simon and Schuster, 1977.

Sprague, Ken, and Bill Reynolds. *The Gold's Gym Book of Bodybuilding.* Chicago: Contemporary Books, Inc., 1983.

Booklets

Food Power: A Coach's Guide to Improving Performance. Rosemont, Illinois: National Dairy Council, 1984.

Scott, Larry. *How to Build Massive Forearms.*

Newsletters

"Gentler Aerobics." *Healthwise*, vol. 9, no. 9 (September 1986).

Lamb, Lawrence. "Weight Training for Energy and Weight Control." *The Health Letter*, vol. 5, no. 4.

————. "Varicose Veins." *The Health Letter*, vol. 8, no. 8.

"Losing Weight and Making Sure You Keep It Off." *Tufts University Diet and Nutrition Newsletter*, vol. 3, no. 12 (February 1986): pp. 3–6.

President's Council on Physical Fitness and Sports. "Development of Muscular Strength and Endurance." *Physical Fitness Research Digest*, Series 4, no. 1 (January 1974).

"Salt and Obesity." *Healthwise*, vol. 9, no. 10 (October 1986). (Excerpted from the *British Medical Journal*, 292:1697, 1986.)

Articles

Allen, Deborah. "Should Kids Lift Weights?" *Family Safety* (Winter 1980–1981): p. 9.

American Academy of Pediatrics Committee on Sports Medicine. "Weight Training and Weight Lifting: Information for the Pediatrician." *The Physician and Sportsmedicine*, vol. 3, no. 11 (1983): pp. 157–161.

Barnes, Ian. "Exercise Is Crucial in New Weight Loss Theory." *The Physician and Sportsmedicine* (February 1984): p. 19.

Boyer, Pamela. "Sunless Tanning: The Best of Both Worlds." *Prevention* (January 1987): pp. 76–78.

Burkett, Lee N., and Michael T. Falduto. "Steroid Use by Athletes in a Metropolitan Area." *The Physician and Sportsmedicine*, vol. 12, no. 8 (August 1984): pp. 69–70, 73–74.

Cannon, Geoffrey, and Hetty Einzig. "Does Dieting Make You Fat?" *Reader's Digest* (November 1986): pp. 134–137.

Charlier, Marj. "Cave Man's Life Is Worth Aping, Doctors Believe." *The Wall Street Journal* (October 21, 1986): p. 1.

Dayton, Laura. "Those Marvelous Machines." *Fit* (September 1984): pp. 73–80.

Derby, Richard E. "Bodybuilding in a Prisoner of War Camp." *IronMan*, vol. 7, no. 2 (October–November 1946): pp. 21, 41.

Elam, Reid. "Warm-up and Athletic Performance: A Physiological Analysis." *NSCA Journal*, vol. 8, no. 2 (1986): pp. 30–32.

Everson, Corinna. "Corinna's Waist-Land." *Muscle and Fitness* (August 1985): pp. 36–41, 195–196.

Everson, Jeff. "Warm Up Before You Warm Up?" *Muscle and Fitness* (August 1986): p. 19.

"Exercise Shown to Reduce Cancer Risk." *Evansville Courier* (January 10, 1986): p. 9. (from the *British Journal of Cancer*, December 1985).

Facinelli, Paul. "Perk Up Your Metabolism and Peel Off Pounds." *Prevention* (March 1985): pp. 57–60.

Ferrigno, Lou. "Lou Ferrigno Answers Your Training Problems." *Muscle Mag International* (May 1984): p. 47.

———. "Lou Ferrigno Answers Your Training Problems." *Muscle Mag International* (September 1984): p. 45.

Foley, Denise. "The Exerciser's Guide to Vitamins and Minerals." *Prevention* (September 1984): pp. 67–73.

"For the Record." *Strength Training for Beauty* (June 1986): pp. 89–90.

Freedson, Patty S., Patricia M. Mihevic, et al. "Physique, Body Composition, and Psychological Characteristics of Female Body Builders." *The Physician and Sportsmedicine*, vol. 11, no. 5 (May 1983): pp. 85–90.

Fry, Andrew C. "The Effect of Weight Training on the Heart." *NSCA Journal*, vol. 8, no. 4 (1986): pp. 38–41.

———. "Weight Room Safety." *NSCA Journal*, vol. 7, no. 4 (1985): pp. 32–33.

Gaines, Charles, and George Butler. "Iron Sisters." *Psychology Today* (November 1983): pp. 64–69.

Gerson, Richard F. "Make Exercise Fun: How to Avoid Becoming an Exercise Dropout." *Shape* (May 1984): pp. 78–80, 128.

Greene, Michelle. "Renew Yourself." *People* (January 6, 1986): pp. 32–42.

Hatfield, Frederick. "Athletes of Iron." *Sports Fitness* (January 1986): pp. 46–51, 71.

Hejna, W. F., W. Buturusis, et al. "Prevention of Sports Injuries in High School Students through Strength Training." *NSCA Journal*, vol. 4, no. 1 (1982): pp. 28–31.

Houtkooper, Linda. "Nutritional Support for Muscle Weight Gain." *NSCA Journal*, vol. 8, no. 1 (1986): pp. 62–63.

IFBB Medical Report. "Healthy and Effective Contest Preparation." *Flex* (October 1985): pp. 82–85, 143.

Katch, Victor, and Frank Katch. "Muscle Soreness and Stiffness." *Muscle and Fitness* (February 1983): p. 27.

Koch, Fred. "Natural Squatting Bar—An Evaluation." *NSCA Journal*, vol. 7, no. 4 (1985): pp. 70–71.

Kozar, B., and Russell M. Lord. "Overuse Injury in the Young Athlete." *The Physician and Sportsmedicine*, vol. 11, no. 7 (July 1983): pp. 116–122.

Lambert, Mike. "The Best Way to Train for Strength?" *Muscle and Fitness* (August 1986): p. 10.

Legwold, Gary. "Does Lifting Weights Harm a Prepubescent Athlete?" *The Physician and Sportsmedicine*, vol. 10, no. 7 (July 1982): pp. 141–144.

McCrerey, Linda. "What to Know Before You Buy." *Sports Fitness* (February 1986): pp. 24–27, 71.

Martin, David. "Jack LaLanne." *IronMan*, vol. 12, no. 4 (December 1952–February 1953): pp. 18, 41–42.

Maur, Glenn. "How Steroids Nearly Killed Me." *Muscle and Fitness* (July 1985): pp. 112–114, 171–173.

Mazer, Eileen. "Natural Remedies For Fluid Retention." *Prevention* (December 1983): pp. 106–112.

Meade, Jeff. "Nutritional Breakthrough of the Eighties: Omega-3." *Prevention* (July 1986): pp. 85–90.

Mentzer, Mike. "Posing and Presentation." *Muscle Mag International* (January 1984): pp. 58–59, 69.

Miller, J. A. "Beginning Weight Training." *Strength and Health* (March 1983): pp. 16–17.

Mollica, Mae. "How Does Training Affect Your Monthly Cycle?" *Flex* (January 1987): pp. 120–121.

National Strength and Conditioning Association. "Position Paper on Anabolic Drug Use by Athletes" (1985).

———. "Position Paper on Prepubescent Strength Training" (1985).

———. "Strength Training and Conditioning for the Female Athlete." *NSCA Journal*, vol. 7, no. 3 (1985): pp. 10–29.

Nutter, June. "Physical Activity Increases Bone Density." *NSCA Journal*, vol. 8, no. 3 (1986): pp. 67–69.

Occhipinti, Mark. "Amino Acid Imbalances." *Muscle Training Illustrated* (October 1986): pp. 7, 9, 22.

Ostler, Scott. "Success of Tigers' Lance Parrish Could Bring the Beef in Baseball." L.A. Times–Washington Post News Service. *Evansville Courier* (September 14, 1984): p. 24.

Pagano, Tony. "Developing Strength." *IronMan* (May 1983): pp. 37, 62, 64.

Pardee, Richard. "Weight Training and Your Heart: New Evidence About Weights and Cholesterol." *Muscle and Fitness* (April 1985): p. 119.

Pauletto, Bruno. "Intensity." *NSCA Journal*, vol. 8, no. 1 (1986): pp. 33–37.

Pechter, Kerry. "A Consumer's Guide to the Amazing Aminos." *Prevention* (March 1985): pp. 133–138.

———. "How Fiber Helps Your Body Stay Well." *Prevention* (September 1985): pp. 50–56.

Pesta, Ben. "Albert Beckles." *Muscle and Fitness* (October 1985): p. 224.

———. "I Beat Drugs With Iron." (Story on Robert Blake.) *Muscle and Fitness* (January 1986): pp. 83–85, 161–166.

Pirie, Lynn. "The Benefits of Getting Strong." *Shape* (August 1986): pp. 45, 108–109.

Rader, Peary. "The Squat—Greatest Single Exercise." *IronMan*, vol. 15, no. 1 (June–July 1955): pp. 22–26, 47.

Rigon, Claude. "Why Act My Age." *IronMan* (July 1982): pp. 32–33, 62, 64, 66, 68.

Shankman, Gary A. "Special Considerations in Conditioning the Young Athlete." *NSCA Journal*, vol. 7, no. 3 (1985): pp. 52–53.

Shealey, Tom. "The Good Fats." *Prevention* (December 1985): pp. 49–54.

Shellock, Frank G. "Physiological, Psychological and Injury Prevention Aspects of Warm-Up." *NSCA Journal*, vol. 8, no. 5 (1986): pp. 24–27.

Slavin, Joanne L., and David J. Joensen. "Caffeine and Sports Performance." *The Physician and Sportsmedicine*, vol. 13, no. 5 (May 1985): pp. 191–193.

Stamford, Bryant. "The Difference Between Strength and Power." *The Physician and Sportsmedicine*, vol. 13, no. 7 (July 1985): p. 155.

———. "Why Do Your Muscles Get Sore?" *The Physician and Sportsmedicine*, vol. 12, no. 11 (November 1984): p. 147.

"Steroid Users May Risk AIDS." *NSCA Journal*, vol. 7, no. 5 (1985): p. 42C.

Stone, Richard. "A Guide to Heavy-Duty Hi Tech." *Flex* (September 1984): pp. 34–42, 107.

Strauss, Richard H., James E. Wright, et al. "Side Effects of Anabolic Steroids in Weight-Trained Men." *The Physician and Sportsmedicine*, vol. 11, no. 12 (December 1983): pp. 87–88, 91–96.

Switzer, Ellen, and Hara E. Marano. "Fashion's New Muscle." *American Health* (October 1984): pp. 64–72.

Tanny, Armand. "Booze: How It Works On Your Liver, Your Muscles, Your Heart." *Muscle and Fitness* (June 1986): pp. 46–47, 158–159.

Taylor, William N. "Gigantic Athletes: The Dilemma of Human Growth Hormone." *The Futurist* (August 1985): pp. 8–12.

———. "Growth Hormone: Preventing Its Abuse in Sports." *Technology Review* (October 1985): pp. 14–15, 30.

———. "Super Athletes Made to Order." *Psychology Today* (May 1985): pp. 63–66.

Todd, Jan. "Strength Training for Female Athletes." *Journal of Physical Education, Recreation, and Dance* (August 1985): pp. 38–39.

Totten, Leo. "Practical Considerations in Strengthening the Prepubescent Athlete." *NSCA Journal*, vol. 8, no. 2 (1986): pp. 38–40.

Tucker, Larry A. "Effect of Weight Training on Self-Concept: A Profile of Those Influenced Most." *Research Quarterly For Exercise and Sport*, vol. 54, no. 4 (1983): pp. 389–397.

Vaughn, Lewis. "Olive Oil Against Cholesterol." *Prevention* (October 1986): p. 34.

Vrijens, J. "Muscle Strength Development in the Pre and Post Pubescent Age." *Medicine and Sport*, vol. 11 (1978): pp. 152–158.

Warner, Russ, and Redd Hall. "Closeup on Carla." *Muscular Development* (June 1986): pp. 58–61.

Wheeler, Keith B. "Carbohydrates: Nutritional Support for Optimal Performance." *NSCA Journal*, vol. 7, no. 4 (1985): pp. 56–57.

Yessis, Michael. "Back Pain: What Causes It." *Muscle and Fitness* (May 1986): pp. 57, 200.

———. "Overtraining." *Muscle and Fitness* (May 1986): pp. 23, 135–138.

Interviews

Ms. Kay Baxter, professional bodybuilder.

Mr. Mike Carter, vice-president for youth and adolescent activities, National Strength and Conditioning Association.

Mr. Dick Conner, powerlifting coach, owner—Pit Barbell Club, Evansville, Indiana.

Ms. Mary Engelland, registered dietitian, YMCA fitness director, Evansville, Indiana.

Dr. Bob Goldman, author, *Death in the Locker Room*.

Mr. Dave Hawk, professional bodybuilder.

Mr. Ash Hayes, executive director, President's Council on Physical Fitness and Sports.

Mr. Jeff King, professional bodybuilder.

Mr. Todd King, amateur bodybuilder

Mr. Bill Norberg, amateur bodybuilder.

Ms. Dona Oliveira, professional bodybuilder.

Ms. Tina Plakinger, professional bodybuilder.

Mr. Tom Platz, professional bodybuilder.

Ms. Nina Schoenbaum, director, Women's Mid-City Bodybuilding Gym, New York City.

Ms. Marjo Selin, professional bodybuilder.

Seminar

Mr. Olympia Seminar, October 12, 1986, Columbus, Ohio.